A journey ir

A THEOLOGICAL NOVEL

Richard P. Belcher

 EVANGELICAL PRESS

EVANGELICAL PRESS
12 Wooler Street, Darlington, Co. Durham, DL1 1RQ, England

First published in the U.S.A. in 1988 by Richbarry Press.
First Evangelical Press edition 1993.
This edition © Evangelical Press 1993

British Library Cataloguing in Publication Data available.

ISBN 0-85234-309-4

Scripture quotations in this publication are from the New King
James Version. Copyright © 1979, 1980, 1982, Thomas Nelson
Inc., Publishers.

Cover illustration by Conny Jude

Printed in Great Britain at The Bath Press, Avon.

Contents

1.
Caught off guard!

On 15 October 1970 I found myself facing the prospect of fulfilling within the next few days a dream I had cherished for two years — the possibility of becoming a pastor. It was not that a church had already extended a call to me, nor that I had even preached a trial sermon. But a pastorless church had contacted me and wanted to talk with me about the possibility of becoming their next pastor. I couldn't believe it.

The church wasn't a large one in any sense — fifty or sixty in attendance on Sunday morning. The salary (though I did not know the amount then) was certainly nothing to write home about. Nor was the church located in any large metropolitan city, or even in a rural county-seat town. Rather it was a country church, out in the middle of almost nowhere, and it was attended by rural people of humble means and ways.

Those facts mattered not at all to a young preacher who was a second-year ministerial student at a local Baptist college. I had only preached a couple of dozen times since I had been converted as a junior in high school, and the thought of preaching every week, of having a church of my own, a people of my own and a pulpit of my own was almost overwhelming.

Many of the rural churches within a sixty-mile radius had depended on the local Baptist college to provide them with preachers and pastors over the years. This arrangement not only supplied the needs of the churches, but was also a useful source of finance for young men seeking to get an education and maybe some practical experience in the process. You can imagine my joy and excitement when one of these churches contacted me and proposed an interview to determine if I would be a possible candidate for their new pastor. The date of the interview was set for 15 October 1970, one week after they telephoned me.

That week between the phone-call and the face-to-face interview seemed interminable — would that day ever arrive? It wasn't that I didn't have anything to occupy my thoughts. Far from it! Wishing to make the best possible impression on their 'interview committee', I tried to anticipate every twist or turn the forthcoming meeting could take.

What would they ask me about doctrine? I tried to do a bit of study by reading a booklet on Baptist beliefs, and I even sought to memorize some key verses in each doctrinal area. Whatever they asked, I decided I would be authoritative in voice, confident in manner and quick in response. I would avoid areas which I knew were controversial or where I felt I was rather weak.

What would they ask me about the denomination? I didn't have a Baptist pedigree — no father who had been a Baptist preacher or deacon; no Sunday School prizes or Holiday Bible School certificates to declare; no sword drill awards to show, or anything like that. Before my conversion in high school I had been nothing. Maybe at least that would evoke more empathy and understanding from them than if I had come from some other 'enemy' denomination. I concluded I would not only have to be authoritative and confident, but I would have to be humble and teachable if areas of denominational life came up. I did make some attempt to cover my ignorance in this area — I read a short history of the denomination and tried to remember a few important men, dates and events.

Would they ask me about a wife? I didn't have one and wasn't really looking for one, but I supposed I could tell them I wasn't against the idea of marriage if something came along.

Thus with great care and concern I prepared for that eventful hour of the interview. Finally the day arrived!

I drove the forty miles from the college campus to the rural setting of the church, planning to arrive well ahead of schedule, and even anticipating a possible emergency with my eight-year-old car. It wouldn't do to be late for this important moment of history. I hardly noticed the fading of daylight nor the approach of darkness as I made my way along the winding roads. It may have been just an ordinary evening for everyone else along that road, as families arrived home from the responsibilities of the day, sat down to supper and relaxed in front of the television. But for me it was the most important day of my life! As I saw it then, what took place in the next few hours could mean the difference between my having a church of my own to pastor or the continuation of my existence as a student who occasionally had a chance to preach. I continued to drill into my head the thought: 'Be confident and authoritative whatever they ask you, but also be humble and teachable.'

The committee was composed of six members — four men and two women. They were extremely friendly and at times seemed to be more ill-at-ease than I was! Perhaps they didn't know any more about what they were doing than I did! This comforted me and bolstered my determination to be confident and authoritative.

They began by asking me about my early life and conversion. I was sure of creating the right impression as I told them I had not been privileged to be reared in a Christian nor a Baptist home, but had rather grown up in an unconverted household. I told them of my salvation experience in some detail, confident that I knew about that event. They were quite touched and I even noticed a tear in one dear lady's eye. I told the truth, and did so with fervour and sincerity. Without being asked, I went on to tell them of those I had won to the Lord since my conversion. They seemed to rejoice greatly with me. We were off to a great start! If only the rest of the interview went as well!

Next they asked me about doctrine, and I found my study had paid off splendidly. Did I believe the Bible? 'Yes,' I replied, and quoted at length 2 Timothy 3:16 - 4:4. Did I believe in salvation by faith alone? 'Absolutely,' I asserted, quoting Scripture again and adding, 'That is one of the main reasons I became a Baptist.' On and on we went, covering the subjects of baptism, the Lord's Supper, the Second Coming of Christ, and as my answers seemed to satisfy them, my confidence and authority grew.

By the time we had finished doctrine, I felt greater confidence when, as I had anticipated, they asked me about the denomination. Did I believe in the denomination's objectives? Was I committed to the denomination's mission programme? My reading of the booklet had again been very useful and I was able to drop a few names, dates and events that they didn't even know. My confidence grew!

Finally, we came to what I felt was the end. I had handled every question with skill and ease. My confidence and authority had grown with each answer. Yet I had maintained a humble attitude through it all. I had handled myself exactly the way I had planned. It appeared I was home and dry when the moderator asked if there were any other questions they wanted to ask me, and a long period of silence followed. I was waiting for him to call the meeting to a conclusion, when all of a sudden one man spoke up. He had only listened previously as the others had participated. Now he had a question to ask the 'young preacher-boy', he said, with what appeared to be a sneer and slight scowl.

'Young man,' he asked, 'are you a Calvinist?'

He caught me completely off guard. I didn't know what a Calvinist was. I had never heard the word 'Calvinist'. I could tell by the tone of his voice and his abrasive spirit that he was no Calvinist, and that whatever a Calvinist was, it must be something nasty — something this church would never call as a pastor.

I saw at once that I had a problem! I wanted to tell them I certainly was not a Calvinist, because obviously that was the answer they wanted. But could I tell them I was not something I couldn't even define? If I admitted that I didn't know what a Calvinist was, would they think I was too uninformed doctrinally to be their pastor? It seemed clear to me by the look on their faces as they awaited my answer that 'Calvinism' (whatever it was) had caused some stir or problem in their church at some point of time in the past. Maybe it was a major problem now and they were looking for someone with great knowledge of the subject who could steer the church in the right direction. Would they call a man who was totally ignorant of a topic which had caused a major rift in their fellowship? Suppose I said, 'No,' to their question, and then they wanted to discuss the subject further, then that would force me to betray not only my ignorance, but also my deceit in answering their question.

I had a decision to make and I had to make it quickly. I decided to fall back on my initial plan to answer with confidence and authority. With inward hesitation and fear, but with the outward air of an expert on the subject, I replied, 'No sir, absolutely not! I find no authority in Scripture for anyone to be a Calvinist!'

The answer seemed to satisfy them as the moment of tension was broken by my reply. We all relaxed once again, and I diplomatically made some statement about having a heavy schedule of work waiting for me back at college. They thanked me for taking time from my studies to come, we prayed, and I was on my way.

Surprisingly, as I made my way back over those winding roads in the dark, my mind was not on whether they would call me as pastor or not but on the question, 'Young man, are you a Calvinist?' And I kept turning over in my mind my answer, in which I had declared, 'No sir, absolutely not! I find no authority in Scripture for anyone to be a Calvinist!'

Had I lied to the committee? My answer of 'No' was correct, I rationalized. How could I be something I couldn't even define at that moment? And my answer of finding no authority in Scripture for anyone being a Calvinist was correct also. I hadn't, to my knowledge, found anything in Scripture that would authorize anyone to be a Calvinist.

But on the other hand, could I possibly be a Calvinist and not know it? If I was, had I told a lie? Suppose I had found things in Scripture that would make people Calvinists and just didn't know it because I didn't know what a Calvinist was?

I determined in my heart as I drove through the night that I was going to find out what a Calvinist was. More than that, I was going to find the answer to the question: 'Young man, are you a Calvinist?' Next time someone asked me that question, I would be ready!

2.
The quest begins

With eager determination I arrived back at campus that evening of 15 October 1970. I had decided as I made the drive through the darkness that I would begin my quest even before I went to bed that night. I realized that the hall of residence of that Baptist college was full of aspiring young preachers. Surely there was one who knew what a Calvinist was! I would go to those who were closest to me and ask them the same question the scowling committee member had asked me: 'Are you a Calvinist?'

It was quite logical that my search should begin with my room-mate, Todd Shelton. Todd was a character, to say the least! He was a few years older than I, and he had led a very colourful life (to hear him tell it — and he did like to tell it!) before his conversion. He was a sought-after preacher, perhaps mostly because of his pre-conversion stories, which so impressed everyone, especially the young people.

Todd also had an eye for the young ladies that worried me sometimes. I shall never forget the night he asked to borrow my car for a date. Knowing his practice and reputation, I lent it to him on the condition that he stay out of Lakeview Park, the local lovers' lane. I guess I really should not have been surprised when about 10.30 that night several of the other students came pounding on my door, laughing and shouting that they had caught me in Lakeview Park, and when they stopped to approach my car, I roared away. I learned from that experience that Todd's word couldn't be trusted and when he returned my car I gave him a good dressing-down for breaking his word and damaging my reputation. But he only gave me his boyish country grin and wouldn't even admit he had been in the park.

As I entered our room that night bent on asking him my question, he was lying on the lower bunk reading a book of strip cartoons. This was his favourite pastime, which took preference even over his homework and his Bible. He looked up, said 'Hello', with his friendly but transparent grin, and went back to his reading. After taking off my coat and hanging it in the cupboard I said, 'Todd, I want to ask you a question!'

'Sounds serious!' Todd replied, perhaps wondering if I was going to come down on him again for something.

I knew no other way to put it, and I really wanted to get to the point, so I asked bluntly, 'Todd, are you a Calvinist?'

'Not me!' he replied quickly and confidently.

Thinking perhaps he was bluffing, as I had before the committee, I next queried, 'What is a Calvinist?'

I realized at that moment that I would probably get an answer in Todd's usual style, which was to know all there was to know about everything even though he didn't. Understanding how that characteristic of Todd's so irritated me at times, I felt even more ashamed of having played the same game with the committee when they had asked me the question about Calvinism.

Without thinking for a moment, and hardly looking up from his book, Todd replied that a Calvinist was a Presbyterian because the name came from John Calvin, the founder of the Presbyterian denomination.

When I asked, 'But what do they believe that might be so offensive to Baptists?' Todd assured me it was that they believed in infant baptism, just like the Roman Catholics.

'Is that all?' I asked, somehow feeling there must be more, and not too sure old Todd was playing fair with me.

'That's it!' he replied.

I must admit, I did feel better about my interview before the committee, if Todd was right, because I had answered their questions on baptism from the Baptist perspective. But if infant baptism was the crux of Calvinism, why had the question even come up? I had spelled out in great depth, and with care, the Baptist view of baptism before the question about Calvinism was ever put. Because of this I had a sneaking suspicion there was more to this subject than

just baptism, especially in the light of what I knew about Todd. I
decided to go along the corridor and see if anyone else had more to
offer on the subject.

As I stepped out into the passageway to begin my pursuit of other
young theologians, I almost immediately bumped into Marvin
Simpson.
      'Have you got a minute, Marvin?' I asked politely.
      'Of course, Ira. What do you need?' he replied.
      Marvin was a really nice fellow! And he was spiritual too —
probably considered by many to be the most spiritual Christian on
campus. He had a prayer life that was unmatched. It was a well-
known fact that he prayed for hours on end, and that you might
stumble on Marvin on his knees in prayer in some very unusual
places on the campus and at some very unusual hours. There was
even a joke that circulated that one day a faculty member couldn't
get into the gents' toilet on the ground floor for two hours. Each time
he went in the light was off, but the cubicle was locked. Finally, a
further check revealed that Marvin was in there praying with the
door locked and the lights off. I never had the nerve to ask Marvin
about the truth or falsity of that story.
      'Marvin, are you a Calvinist?' I asked quietly, not wishing the
whole floor of students to hear my question.
      'Ira,' replied Marvin, with his usual warm and fuzzy spiritual
voice, 'that sounds like a doctrinal question to me, and I really don't
know too much about doctrine. All I want to do is to love and serve
Jesus, and help others to do the same.'
      I tried again. 'Have you ever even heard the word "Calvinist"
before?'
      'Well, yes, I suppose,' he said reluctantly. 'But I can't recall
exactly where or when. I really think you would be better off seeking
the Lord rather than these theological subjects, but if you insist on
finding out, why don't you try Ron Masters?' he suggested. 'His dad
is a pastor. He probably would know.'

After thanking Marvin for his help, I made my way down the far
end of the passage to Ron Masters' room. True, Ron's dad was a
preacher, but I had never possessed much confidence in Ron's call
to the ministry. He was a likeable enough person, but seemed to be
a square peg in a round hole as a ministerial student. His real interest

was the anatomy of the human body and medicine. He had books upon books on his shelves in his room which dealt with such subjects. We all were convinced that he could name every bone in the human body. It was a standing joke that he knew more about the human body and medicine than the school doctor, whom many considered to be a quack and a pill-pusher. I had often wondered if Ron had become a preacher to please his father.

I found him as usual reading from one of his medical journals. He was alone in the room, for which I was glad, because I didn't want to converse with two persons at the same time on my delicate subject.

I introduced my question by saying, 'Ron, your dad's a preacher, and you've had a lot of experience in the local church. Would you call yourself a Calvinist?'

He replied with some caution saying, 'Well, I've never really made a study of the subject, but from what I have gathered from my father when he spoke of theology, we [he always spoke in the plural, giving his father's view and his own as one] would not be Calvinists.'

'Why not?' I asked.

'Well, from what I remember,' he replied, obviously probing his own powers of recollection, 'Calvinists don't believe in evangelism, missions, or even a public invitation for men to come to Christ.'

'Why not?' I asked again.

'Well,' he said hesitatingly, 'it has something to do with their view of predestination and election, but I'm not sure exactly what. Why don't you ask Charlie Hester? He should know.'

Charles Hester was the campus brain. He was a final-year student, was always at the head of the dean's list, and had never had anything less than an A in any of his subjects while in college. No doubt he would go on some day and teach — he was smart enough. You always felt intimidated if you got caught in a discussion with him, let alone knocking on his door and instigating one.

But by now I was desperate. I had been told that Calvinism was Presbyterianism, and referred especially to the baptism of infants. I had been told I would be better off to go and pray and seek to be spiritual rather than ask questions about doctrine. I had been told that Calvinists didn't believe in missions, evangelism, or public invitations because of their view of predestination and election. I felt as if I had just interviewed the three blind men who tried to describe an elephant from just their single perspective of research. Somehow I wasn't convinced I had got to the heart of the matter yet, as far as a definition was concerned.

Hesitantly, I knocked softly on Charlie Hester's door, not wishing to disturb him if he was asleep. The door opened to a dimly lit room. The only light was a lamp on Charlie's desk. It was obvious he was studying (what else did Charlie ever do besides study?), as the books and papers were piled high in various places.

He invited me in with a look and a tone of voice that said, 'Don't stay too long!' I apologized for the late intrusion, but assured him I had a problem which no one in the hall had been able to answer, and that he was my last resort. He didn't even invite me to sit down, a clear hint he wanted me gone as soon as possible. So with a deep breath, and a conviction that the question couldn't wait till morning, I asked him, 'Charlie, are you a Calvinist?'

His reply was direct and quick: 'Certainly not.'

As he spoke I wasn't a bit concerned that he might be just bluffing like Todd. When Charlie spoke, people received it as the gospel.

Not knowing how far I could push it without being asked to leave so he could get back to his studies, I quickly blurted out, 'Why not?'

'Because Calvinism with its strict view of predestination and election, whereby God has supposedly chosen only to save a few elect persons, and also has decreed the remainder of the non-elect to an eternal hell, robs man of his personal decision for Christ and his freedom of choice. Such a position also immediately torpedoes the church's work of evangelism and missions.'

His statement staggered me! How could anyone ever believe that? No wonder the fellow on the interview committee asked his question with such a scowl! How glad I was I had given the answer I did and with such conviction!

It was obvious it was time for me to leave Charlie's room. Yet how surprised I was when, instead of dismissing me, Charlie offered more information on the subject! He said there was an acrostic often used to summarize the Calvinist position. It used the word TULIP. The 'T' stood for 'total depravity'. The 'U' stood for 'unconditional election'. The 'L' stood for 'limited atonement'. The 'I' stood for 'irresistible grace'. The 'P' stood for the 'perseverance of the saints'.

Convinced I was finally getting somewhere in beginning to understand this subject of Calvinism, though it was obvious I didn't agree with the viewpoint, I wrote the acrostic on a piece of scrap paper as follows:

T Total depravity
U Unconditional election
L Limited atonement
I Irresistible grace
P Perseverance of the saints

Charlie told me he didn't have time to explain these areas of doctrine to me more fully, but offered to do so at some future point in time. It was the friendliest Charlie had ever been to me. Perhaps he was happy to see one of the younger students take an interest in theological pursuits, or at least be concerned with more than girls and reading strip cartoons.

I returned to my room sensing I had made some progress, but not much. Not wanting to forget my 'research' of the night, I made a few notes concerning Calvinism. I had been told the following:

1. Calvinists are Presbyterians.
2. Calvinists believe in infant baptism.
3. Calvinists believe in the predestination and election of a few to eternal life.
4. Calvinists believe in the predestination of all others to an eternal death.
5. Calvinists deny man freedom of choice.
6. Calvinists rob man of a personal decision for Christ.
7. Calvinists deny the church its work of evangelism and missions.
8. Calvinists do not believe in a public invitation.
9. Calvinists believe in total depravity.
10. Calvinists believe in unconditional election.
11. Calvinists believe in limited atonement.
12. Calvinists believe in irresistible grace.
13. Calvinists believe in perseverance of the saints.

   As I got ready for bed (by now it was close to midnight and my body was tired out — it had been a long day), my mind kept turning over these concepts. I wasn't satisfied that I had really found the answer to my question. In fact, I didn't even understand what I had been told that evening concerning Calvinism. What is total depravity? What is unconditional election? Then as I crawled into bed and turned the light off, my mind began to formulate further plans to research my subject. My next step would be to interview certain faculty members of my Baptist college. Surely these men of education and knowledge could tell me what a Calvinist is. I began to think of questions to ask when I interviewed them: 'Is it true that all Calvinists are Presbyterians? Is it true that all Calvinists believe in infant baptism? Is it true......................zzzzzzzzz!'

3.
What the professors said

I didn't exactly shoot out of bed the next morning like a rocket. In fact, I think my mind reached the launching pad before my body. I have often wished I could be as awake early in the morning as I am when I go to bed at night, and vice-versa. But I did rise before most of the other fellows, including Todd.

After gulping down my breakfast, I hurried to my first lecture — the old eight o'clock one, which everybody wants on his schedule (so he can finish early in the day) but which no one wants to attend. It seemed this morning that Dr Ambers would drone on for ever. My pencil took notes, but my heart was elsewhere. I had a free hour coming up and planned to make the rounds of the professors' offices to book interviews with them as soon as possible.

When the lecture was finally over, I made my way to the closest office of one of the four men I wanted to interview — Dr Lollar. It was right next door to the room I had just left. Dr Lollar taught Bible courses to many of the first-year students, so I knew him from the previous year and hoped he remembered me as well. Besides that, he was a gentleman — kind, considerate, sensitive to the students' needs, and always willing to spend time with them. What better place to begin my time with the faculty on my subject of interest than with him?

When I knocked gingerly at his door, I was met with a friendly 'Come on in!' I told him I would like to make an appointment with him to discuss an important issue that had unexpectedly arisen in my

life, and to my surprise he responded with, 'How about right now?
There's no better time than the present!'

I had planned to see each of the professors later in the week, and
to lay careful strategy for the interview. So when Dr Lollar said he
was available right now, I stammered for a few moments, not
knowing where to begin. Finally I plunged straight in with the
question that the committee member had hit me with, and I asked,
'Dr Lollar, are you a Calvinist?'

A friendly smile spread over his face. At least he wasn't going to
get annoyed at the question. But he really didn't help me very much
when he replied, 'Well, young man, that's hard to answer. I suppose
some people would call me a Calvinist, and some would say I'm not
a Calvinist.'

I wondered at the time what kind of an answer that was. Was
Calvinism so elusive in its definition that no one could know who
or what a Calvinist was? Why, then, the big fuss over the question:
'Are you a Calvinist?'

I was about to ask another question to carry the conversation
further to more enlightened ground when Dr Lollar freely continued: 'Personally, I don't like the use of theological terms applied to
me and I don't like to put them on other people. Oh, how many
phrases we throw around today — Calvinism, Arminianism,
dispensationalism, modernism, liberalism. fundamentalism,
conservativism, evangelicalism, premillennialism, postmil-
lennialism, amillennialism, pre-tribulationalism — need I say
more? Those are man-made terms and man-made systems, and I will
not associate my name with anything except what is taught in the
Bible.'

'Yes,' I asked, 'but don't these terms help us state in a nutshell
what we believe the Bible teaches?'

'Well, that might be true,' he explained, 'if everyone used the
terms to mean exactly the same thing. But when you refer to me
using one of your terms, that term can only be true of me if you and
I define it in the same manner. If you mean one thing by the term and
I mean something else by the same term, then I am not what you say
I am. And if I call myself by a term and you have a different
definition of that term from the one I have, then I am not in your eyes
what I say I am. Thus the use of theological terms becomes very
confusing.'

I was really puzzled now. So I asked boldly, 'Then if someone asks me if I am a Calvinist, or if I am something else according to one of these theological terms, what am I supposed to say?'

'Just tell them that you believe the Bible — it is your authority, and if the Bible teaches it, then you believe it. If the Bible doesn't teach it, then you don't believe it. It's that simple!'

It may have sounded simple to him, but it didn't to me. I was more confused than ever. Seeing I was getting nowhere, and not wishing to offend him by further probing, I thanked Dr Lollar for his time and excused myself. On the way back to the hall of residence, I thought of several questions I should have asked him.

If we cannot use any terms to refer to our beliefs, but can only say, 'I believe the Bible,' how can we use even the term 'Baptist' to refer to us as a group? Doesn't that term speak of some theological beliefs?

Secondly, don't different persons say the Bible teaches different things? How are we to distinguish true doctrine from false doctrine if we don't use some theological terms to conveniently summarize our position?

Finally, if you can't use theological terms, then you can't use any terms at all, even Bible terms like justification, redemption, sanctification, etc., lest someone else have a different definition of that term. You could only say, 'If the Bible teaches it, I believe it!,' but you could never say, 'I believe in justification,' out of fear that someone might define it differently. Such logic would destroy communication altogether. After all, words are symbols for concepts, and if you cannot use any word as a symbol for a concept, or concepts, for fear of being misunderstood, then you couldn't even speak, let alone preach.

Why hadn't I thought of these arguments when in Dr Lollar's office? That's the way it is in so many of my theological discussions and debates — I think of all the answers after the debate is over. But still, I guess it's better to think of them after the debate than not at all.

When I walked into my room back at the hall, Todd met me at the door smiling from ear to ear. 'Guess what!', he exclaimed.

'You're engaged again!' I shot back, getting ready to congratulate him again. To be honest, I had lost track of the number of times

he had been engaged in his first year, and really couldn't be very
enthusiastic about another one. I had been bracing myself for the
first engagement of his second year.

'No!' he said with a frown. 'The church rang and wants you to
ring them back about a date for a trial sermon!'

'A trial sermon? Me — preach a trial sermon? Wow!'

The date for the trial sermon was set for the last Sunday in
October. Really, it would be two trial sermons, as I would preach for
them Sunday morning and Sunday evening, after which they would
vote to call me or not to call me as their pastor. Could it be that I was
just a few days away from becoming a pastor? Now I had two things
to think about — the trial sermons and the answer to the question:
'Are you a Calvinist?'

My next interview with a faculty member was several days after
the initial one. I was to meet Dr Sisk in his office at 4 p.m. that day.
He taught church history, seemed to be a very knowledgeable man,
and also open to the students.

I had decided in the interval between these interviews to take a
different approach from the one I had adopted with Dr Lollar.
Instead of asking, 'Are you a Calvinist?' I was going to be more
subtle. It seemed that the question, 'Are you a Calvinist?' immediately put men on the defensive.

So I began a little differently with Dr Sisk. I said, 'Dr Sisk, I have
run across a situation in a local church where I need, if it is possible,
to know the definition of a Calvinist. Could you help me?'

I had been careful to add the 'if it is possible' in case he answered
like Dr Lollar. How surprised and happy I was when he said, 'Well,
let's see if we can help you.'

He continued, 'Calvinism is a system of theology which has been
very influential down through history since the Reformation times.
It's named after its founder, John Calvin, who was also the founder
of the Presbyterian movement, but by no means has Calvinism been
confined to Presbyterians. Why, even some of our greatest Baptists
of the past were Calvinists. In fact, the early Baptist movements in
England and in the United States were very strongly Calvinistic.'

That was news to me! And it would be news to Todd, who
thought all Calvinists were Presbyterians. What's more, that meant

that if Baptists had been Calvinists, then infant baptism was not the heart and crux of Calvinism. Wrong again, room-mate Todd!

Dr Sisk went on: 'Why don't I suggest some books for you to read on the subject, and when you have finished them, we can get together and talk about what you have found?'

Gladly I accepted his list, which included *Sermons on the Sovereignty of God* by C. H. Spurgeon; *The Sovereignty of God* by Arthur W. Pink; and *The Reformed Doctrine of Predestination* by Loraine Boettner.

I recognized the name Spurgeon — the greatest Baptist preacher of modern times. I just had to ask Dr Sisk, 'Was Spurgeon a Calvinist?'

'Absolutely!' he replied.

'A five-point Calvinist?' I asked (glad that Charlie had given me the acrostic).

'He certainly was!' Dr Sisk declared emphatically.

I so much appreciated Dr Sisk's help, but I had to ask two more questions before leaving to do some reading.

'Does the Calvinist view of predestination and election torpedo' (I used Charlie's word) 'evangelism and missions?' I asked that in the light of learning that Spurgeon was a Calvinist. It didn't seem consistent that Spurgeon could be a Calvinist if that view effectively did away with missions and evangelism.

'No, not necessarily,' he replied. 'Some Calvinists, whom we call "hyper-Calvinists", have been extreme in their views and no longer have a burden for a lost world. But some of the balanced Calvinists, like Spurgeon and George Whitefield and others, have been some of the great soul-winners of church history.'

'One more question, Dr Sisk. Are you a Calvinist?'

He smiled and laughed a little. 'No, I would say I am about a three- or four- point Calvinist. I have trouble with limited atonement and irresistible grace.'

I left his office much more satisfied than after the interview with Dr Lollar. I had a list of three books to read and I was much the wiser. I had learned that not all Calvinists have been Presbyterians. I had learned that infant baptism is not part and parcel of Calvinism. I had learned that some of the greatest Baptists of history had been Calvinists. I had learned that Calvinism does not necessarily do away with evangelism and missions. I had learned there are balanced

Calvinists and extreme Calvinists. I had learned that the average person (including the young preachers I had talked to the night before) didn't really know very much about Calvinism. I had learned my search was just beginning.

Before beginning my reading, I decided to make my last professorial interview. This final meeting was with Dr Bloom, who taught theology. He was a brilliant man — so brilliant that most of the students hadn't the foggiest idea what he was saying in class. When a student would stop his lecture to ask a question, he would get very upset. Then as he answered the questions we could usually understand what he was saying, but the only problem was that he was always in a very bad mood when he answered questions. If anyone ever doubted his view, he became very angry and even castigated the questioner.

Thus it was with some apprehension that I entered his office several days later at the appointed time. I sat waiting for almost five minutes (which was his usual practice—many said it was to humble the student and to show him how important the professor was). I wondered if he had forgotten me. Finally he looked up, and not even smiling, asked me what I wanted.

I began carefully: 'Sir, I have run across a problem in a local church which requires me to understand what Calvinism is. Could you help me?'

Well, I must have struck a tender nerve, because he took off!

'I don't know why anyone would want to study Calvinism! It is the most absurd system of theology ever to exist. I do not know how anyone could possibly believe that God before eternity began sat on his tyrannical, heavenly throne and passed the human race before his face, and in an arbitrary, dictatorial manner chose to save some and damn others.'

Then he recited a little poem, words God supposedly spoke before eternity when he chose the elect and did whatever he did regarding the non-elect. I must say, he recited this piece of poetry with much bitterness and spite, which made me feel quite uncomfortable:

Eenie, meenie, minie, mow,
On to heaven *you* will go.
Eenie, meenie, minie, mow,
You will make the fires glow!

Then turning to me with fire in his eyes, he asked, 'Is that the way God did it, young man?'

Honestly, I wished he would stop so I could excuse myself and leave. But he was not about to end his tirade.

'Calvinism is totally unscriptural. It is akin to blasphemy. It presents a God of injustice and terror. Some Calvinists have even declared that the streets of hell will be paved with babies who were not of the elect. If you want to find out about Calvinism, go and read about how John Calvin killed Servetus!'

He was beginning to irritate me now. I had only come to seek light and understanding. I was not a Calvinist, and so his words did not apply to me. I felt he was being unfair and unjust himself by accusing me of being a Calvinist and of all the supposed atrocities of Calvinism.

I shouldn't have done it, but I just couldn't resist. I asked him, 'Sir, where can I find that statement about hell being paved with babies?' I was sincere in the question, but I also wanted to check him in his tracks, because he always said in lectures, 'Don't make a claim in this class unless you can back it up with documentation.'

He continued his tirade: 'Young man, I've been studying theology longer than you have been alive. I have studied these issues in the original languages. I have written papers and books for the best publishing houses of the land. I have forgotten more theology than you have ever learned. Don't ask me for documentation. Be a scholar and go and find it for yourself.'

With that he excused himself and turned back to his papers. I managed a weak, 'Thank you, sir,' and left feeling somewhat scarred in my soul. Besides what I had learned from Dr Lollar and Dr Sisk, I had now learned from Dr Bloom that Calvinism is a very controversial subject and that people, even dignified scholars, could get very emotional when they discussed it.

4.
A sad story

When I arrived back at my room in the hall of residence, I was still emotionally upset due to my joust with Dr Bloom. I really didn't feel like doing much more on the subject at the moment, but I knew I had better make some notes while the matter was fresh in my mind.

I pulled from my pocket the piece of scrap paper that I had used on the first night of the search to record the acrostic and my observations from the discussions with the students. I now recorded this material in a notebook, with further notations concerning what I had learned from the professors. I wrote as follows:

1. Calvinists are Presbyterians. This is not necessarily so. Though the term 'Calvinism' gets its name from the founder of the Presbyterian Church, Calvinism influenced Baptists in their theologies down through history both in England and the United States. Some of the greatest Baptist preachers of the past were Calvinists.

2. Calvinists believe in infant baptism. Obviously this too is untrue, if many Baptists through history have been Calvinists.

3. Calvinists believe in the predestination and election of a few to eternal life. This appears to be so, but I wonder if it could really be true in the light of the fact that so many Baptists of the past were Calvinists?

4. Calvinists believe in the predestination of all others except the elect to eternal death. This too appears to be true, but I am again puzzled how so many Baptists of the past could have believed such a thing.

5. Calvinists deny freedom of choice. This appears to be true, but further research is needed in the light of the fact that so many Baptists in history were Calvinists.

6. Calvinists rob man of a personal decision for Christ. This appears to be true also, but again further research is needed on the same grounds.

7. Calvinists do not believe in evangelism and missions. This appears to be false, especially if Charles H. Spurgeon and George Whitefield were Calvinists.

8. Calvinists do not believe in invitations whereby men would be challenged to confess Christ. My research on this point has not proved it to be true or false.

9. Calvinists believe in total depravity. I have found no evidence that this is false. Further research is necessary to establish its truth or falsity, and to find a definition of the term as used by Calvinists.

10. Calvinists believe in unconditional election. As for number 9.

11. Calvinists believe in limited atonement. As for number 9.

12. Calvinists believe in irresistible grace. As for number 9.

13. Calvinists believe in perseverance of the saints. As for number 9.

Next, I registered several other observations in my notebook concerning Calvinism:

1. There are Calvinists and there are hyper-Calvinists, according to Dr Sisk, although I must admit I do not know the difference at the moment.

2. The average person does not know very much about Calvinism, even though he may think he does. Even the student preachers on campus are rather ignorant of the subject.

3. The subject of Calvinism is a highly controversial one, and many people have a hard time discussing it without becoming very emotional.

I didn't manage to do much further research on the subject for the next couple of months. Things were happening so quickly! The church did call me as pastor, but only after I insisted on a further discussion with the interview committee.

Because I couldn't get the conviction out of my mind that I had not been fully honest with them, I insisted that I see them again, even before preaching the trial sermon. When we met on Saturday afternoon, I simply laid before them the fact that I had been troubled over their question concerning Calvinism. I told them that it wasn't their question that bothered me, but my answer. I admitted that when they asked me that question, I really didn't know exactly what a Calvinist was, and said I was sorry if I had deceived them. I told them that to my knowledge I was not a Calvinist, but I didn't want them to call me as pastor thinking I was an expert on the subject, or if being an expert on the subject was a prerequisite. I apologized, asked for their forgiveness, and told them I would understand if they wanted to withdraw their invitation to preach a trial sermon. I fully expected they might do just that.

How surprised and overjoyed I was when they were even more insistent that I come for a trial message! They so much appreciated my honesty in the matter, and rather than my confession driving a wedge between us, it seemed to fuse our hearts together further.

They admitted they were not experts on Calvinism either. They only knew the word because their last pastor, a man named Jim Mitchell, had become a Calvinist in the middle of his service there. It seemed to change his entire ministry and personality.

Sensing our hearts were being knitted together in this time of sharing, and thinking perhaps this piece of information might be helpful to me not only in my search, but also if I became their pastor, I asked, 'How did Calvinism change his personality and ministry?'

'Oh, he was different!' offered one of the ladies.

'But how?' I probed. 'Did it affect his ministry? Did it affect his family life? Did it affect his relationship with people?'

As we sat and talked for about an hour the following picture emerged, which seemed to prove that their former pastor underwent a strange metamorphosis when he became a Calvinist.

For one thing, he began constantly to use the terms 'Calvinism' and 'Arminianism' in the pulpit, along with other terms which were foreign to the people. His messages became theological lectures instead of biblical sermons. He so enjoyed this new approach that he would go on for well over an hour in each sermon, almost daring anyone to disagree with him and even indicating it was a sign of a lack of spirituality if someone did not enjoy his sermons. His sermons became so theological that each one was something of a dissertation on one of the five points of Calvinism. He constantly used 'thee' and 'thou' as if he were a preacher of years past.

His attitude was so belligerent that he shouted one day, 'If this be heresy, then thou shalt build a fire, and thou shalt make it hot, and thou shalt burn me at the stake. Better men than I have been put to death for these doctrines.' It was as if he almost expected and wanted people to disagree with what he was preaching.

Further, he stopped challenging men to come to Christ. He refused to give any kind of a public invitation, which in our denomination, I realized, was akin to heresy. No one was ever converted under his ministry after he became a Calvinist, and his whole concern was to make Calvinists out of people rather than Christians.

He began to publish long theological definitions in the bulletins from confessions of faith dated hundreds of years ago. He began to pass out a 'catechism' urging the people to teach it to their children. The church family thought that smacked of Roman Catholicism.

He almost completely gave up visiting, not even people in hospital. He didn't want to spend time with people, only with the Lord and in study.

I asked with great interest, seeing I might be the next pastor, if the church was against a pastor studying and preparing sermons.

They assured me they were not. They realized their pastor needed much time with the Lord if he was to feed them and minister the Word of God with power. It was just that this man's Calvinism seemed to make him insensitive to people and their needs. It seemed to back him into a shell from which he refused to emerge. If anyone wanted to join him in his shell, they could. But if not, that was their problem, and he had no responsibility towards them.

Finally, the deacons met with him, and it was not a pretty scene, they said. He accused them of having unregenerate and reprobate minds. He told them they had no right to question what he preached in the pulpit, nor how he conducted his time through the day. Eventually after much heartache and sorrow, he resigned and left, calling them names that would place them in the category of the lost. He had gone to pastor another church, but they understood he was having the same problem there. And he had taken a very small group of people with him as he left the church.

'What a sad story!' I thought as I drove back to college. Many
questions flew through my mind. Is this what Calvinism does to a
man? Is this why some folk get so emotional when they talk about
the subject? Was this man one of those 'hyper-Calvinists' that Dr
Sisk had mentioned, or was he a true representative of Calvinism?
Was this why Dr Bloom was so upset that I was studying the subject
of Calvinism — he thought I might end up like this man? Had he
seen other young men go that way? Would I go that way if I
continued my research?

Though my mind was totally absorbed with these thoughts as I
travelled back to college, and then hurried to get ready for a supper
engagement, something happened that night that relieved the tension and sorrow produced by the picture of a man's ministry ruined
by Calvinism. I met the girl I would eventually marry! How far away
those afternoon thoughts of Calvinism became as I sat opposite her
at the supper table of a friend who was trying to play matchmaker
between us! I had only come to dinner at her undeniable insistence.
I saw no way, before I arrived, that this girl could be all that my
matchmaking friend had claimed. But she was all of that and even
more! The only problem was that she was going out with someone
else. I returned to my hall of residence at the end of the evening
committed to the saying: 'Prayer changes things.' And then I smiled
and almost chuckled as I thought, 'What would a Calvinist think of
that idea?'

5.
As bad as could be?

Little did I realize when I accepted the pastorate of Lime Creek Baptist Church how much time such an obligation would consume. In fact, those next few weeks through and after the Christmas break, I had no time of my own. Between studies, sermon preparation, church visitation, hospital calls, etc., etc., I spent the busiest two months of my life. I hardly even had time to enquire if God had answered my prayer concerning the young lady I had met, although I did find time to keep praying in that direction.

It was over the Christmas holidays of 1970 that I found some time to read the books Dr Sisk had suggested, plus several others on the subject of Calvinism. I decided to read them in a very objective manner, not reacting according to whether I agreed or disagreed with the authors, but rather with the purpose of understanding what they were saying. I especially tried to arrive at a clear definition of each of the five points of Calvinism. Then when college started once again in January, I would seek out Dr Sisk, who had promised future help when I had read the books. I would bounce my definitions off him to see if I had properly analysed the subject.

Therefore on about the third day of term in the new year of January 1971, with several pages of notes in my hands, I made my way to Dr Sisk's office for an appointed meeting. He welcomed me cordially, and expressed great joy that I had not let the matter die, but was pursuing the study.

I jumped right in by telling Dr Sisk my approach. I said, 'Dr Sisk, I am going to give you the definition of the five points of Calvinism as I have discovered them in my reading, and I want you to correct me if I am wrong at any point.'

He agreed, and we were off as we plunged into the subject of total depravity.

Cautiously I said, 'As I understand it, total depravity does not mean that all men are as sinful in their actions and deeds as they could possibly be. Rather total depravity speaks of man's nature and potential rather than his actions and deeds. Am I right so far?'

'You are right,' he said with pride over what he was hearing.

I continued: 'When someone says that men are totally depraved sinners, it does not mean that every, or any, man will ever come, or has ever come to the full extent of sinful actions possible from his nature. Not even a Hitler, as evil as he was, ever came to the full end of the potential nature of sin that he possessed. Rather he was a picture of part of the potential of a sinful nature. Am I making myself clear, or is that confusing?'

'You are making yourself clear, and you are exactly correct.'

'Well,' I said as I caught my breath, somewhat surprised myself at what was coming from my brain and mouth, 'I've found it helpful in my thinking to use the illustration of a stick of dynamite to speak of man's sinful nature as the Calvinist would see it. That stick of dynamite has the nature of dynamite whether it ever explodes and destroys buildings and people or not. Regardless, it is still a stick of dynamite and it has the nature of dynamite even if it never explodes. So man by nature is a sinner; and even if he never comes to the full potential of sin that is in him, he still possesses a sinful nature that is thoroughly depraved and evil.'

'Did you consider why man never comes to the full potential of his sinful nature ?' interrupted Dr Sisk .

'Well, since I am trying to stay objective in this discussion, I would reply that the Calvinist would say it is because of God's grace shown through government, family, the preaching of the gospel, etc. I think the Calvinist would call that "common grace".'

Dr Sisk nodded approval and agreement, so I continued.

'Now, the Calvinist says that the reason men have such a hard time understanding the term "total depravity" is because it speaks of man's nature and not his actions. Many automatically conclude that total depravity speaks of actions, and they know men are not totally evil; therefore, total depravity, they say, could not be true. But the Calvinist insists that it must be remembered that total depravity speaks of man's *nature* and not his *deeds*. If we keep this in mind, the Calvinist says, then total depravity is understandable.'

Dr Sisk looked surprised. 'You have been giving this some thought, haven't you?' he said, with evident amazement. 'Now, have you considered how this depravity relates to the Fall and man's present ability to become a Christian?'

I scrambled through my notes for the section where I had recorded something concerning this area of thought, and I began again.

'Yes, the Calvinist says' (and I was careful to stay objective over the matter) 'that man is totally depraved because of the Fall. When Adam fell he plunged the whole human race into sin. That is, we all have a sinful nature now because of the fall of Adam. This depraved nature, which came by the Fall, includes a total inability in the area of spiritual things. The Fall left man's mind blind and ignorant of spiritual matters. He cannot understand things in the spiritual realm unless the Spirit of God enlightens him. Furthermore, the Fall left man's emotions corrupt and turned in the direction of sin rather than towards God. His emotions will not move towards or centre on God unless God enables him. That means he cannot love God in his own strength, will not seek or desire God, nor the things of God, but rather he desires and will continually seek the things of sin.'

I looked up at this point to see if Dr Sisk had any questions or anything to add. 'What about man's will?' he asked. 'Was man so corrupted by the Fall, and yet his will left uncorrupted?'

'No,' I continued. 'Man's will is fallen also. The will is no independent entity that escaped the results of the Fall. Even if the will was not corrupted by the Fall (which is not the case according to the Calvinist), it could not choose God because of the results of the Fall in the other areas of man — the blind mind and the corrupt emotions would cause the will to choose anything but God.

'Thus, man is in a bad helpless state. His mind is blind to the things of God. His emotions are corrupt and set upon sin. And his will is fallen and powerless. That means man has no power within himself to come to God. Not only does he not desire God, unless God gives him the desire, but he also lacks the power or the will to come to God. Unless God gives him the desire, the will and the power to come to Christ, man is lost for ever.'

Dr Sisk interrupted again. He had a class coming up and had to draw this session to a close. He asked me one more question, promising to continue the discussion again very soon. He asked, 'In seeking to stay objective in this search you have undertaken, what problems and questions do you see that you must ask the Calvinist?'

He was correct. Some questions had gone through my mind as I read the assigned books and even now as I had sought to put the Calvinist position into words. Thinking back over what had been said, I pulled several questions from the back of my mind.

'First, for one thing, I would have to ask the Calvinist to explain to me the "whosoever will" statements in the Bible. Surely it seems that if the Bible says, "Whosoever will may come," that man is able to come to God if he so wills.

'Second, even further, I would ask the Calvinist about man's responsibility to come to Christ. If man is not able to come to Christ, how can God hold him responsible and judge him eternally for not coming to Christ?

'Third, I would ask the Calvinist, if men will not desire and come to God unless God gives them the desire and power, what is the basis on which God decides whom he will bring to himself, and whom he will not?'

I realized the answer to that question would soon be answered when Dr Sisk and I got together to discuss unconditional election.

When I arrived back at my room, I found Todd grinning from ear to ear again. He put down his book and asked once again with his usual fervour, 'Guess what?'

'Who is she?' I asked, rather impatiently and without much interest. Old Todd usually only got that excited over a girl. I figured he had either just met a new one or had just got engaged to an old one. Either way, it probably wouldn't last very long. Thus today's joy would be tomorrow's indifference.

'Her name,' he said, pausing before letting it out, 'is Terry Lynn Lasitor.'

'Terry Lynn Lasitor!' I exclaimed. 'What about Terry Lynn Lasitor? Don't tell me you've got your eye on her?'

Terry Lynn Lasitor was the girl I had met at the dinner, who had been an object of my prayers ever since. She wouldn't give old Todd a second look — she had too much class. She would see right through him. That didn't mean he wouldn't try to date her if he got a chance, even though he knew I had a deep interest in her.

'No!' he said. 'Would your old room-mate and chum try to cut in on you?'

I didn't answer that, because I might have had to say, 'Yes, if he could,' if I answered honestly.

'Well, what about Terry Lynn Lasitor?' I asked again.

My heart almost stopped as Todd finally said it: 'She broke up with her old boyfriend over the Christmas holidays, and now the door's wide open for you. I thought you and I might make it a double date on Wednesday evening and take the girls to church.'

I didn't doubt his information. Todd knew about all the girls, available and unavailable, within a twenty-mile radius. He had better information contacts than the FBI.

He went on to explain that he had his eye on a girl who went to the same church as Terry, and it would be a good excuse to ask her out if we could make up a foursome.

And then he said, 'Could you lend me five dollars for the date that night? The information I just gave you ought to be worth a least that much!' he teased.

6.
God's choice or man's?

Events at this point of time were unfolding so quickly in my life that I didn't know if I could stand much more excitement. As well as continuing my college studies, I was pastor of a church, preaching and ministering to my people each week. And I could soon be involved in two searches — the search or pursuit of a young lady and the pursuit of a theological viewpoint which wouldn't let go of me!

Actually, both pursuits were already under way. The theological one was in top gear, and the pursuit of the young lady had possibilities of soon moving from low gear into second.

I hadn't taken up Todd's suggestion that we make it a double date the next Wednesday evening (and not because he wanted to borrow the five dollars). I was somewhat shy and feared a possible rejection if I contacted her by phone. Instead I suggested to him that we go to the girls' church the next Wednesday evening (my pastoral duties spared me the Wednesday evening service because of the distance from college).

I further suggested that we play it by ear when we got to the services, and see if things might open up for us to take them home. I had no idea whether Terry would be interested in me or not, and I thought if I visited her church with her now in an unattached status, she might give me a clue or some means of encouragement if she was interested.

This suggestion didn't go down too well with Todd. He loved to ring a girl up and 'thrill her' (as he put it) with the invitation to a date with him. But there wasn't much he could do but go along with my suggestion, seeing I had the car and the money. We decided we would go that next Wednesday evening. No use wasting any time!

On Wednesday afternoon I had my second appointment with Dr Sisk, at which time we were to talk about unconditional election. Armed again with my notes, we engaged in conversation late that afternoon, following the same procedure as before.

I began eagerly and with much more confidence than in the first meeting: 'Unconditional election is the act of God whereby he chooses a group of people before the foundation of the world to be his own. This group of people is known as "the elect".' I looked for approval from Dr Sisk, and for a sign to continue or halt for discussion.

He led me on by asking, 'What was the basis of God's choice of these elect?'

'The basis of God's choice,' I continued, 'was nothing within these people themselves. It wasn't any goodness, because we have already seen the Calvinist's belief in total depravity.' (I wasn't yet aware of the difference between infralapsarianism and supra-lapsarianism, that is, whether God's decree to choose a people came before or after the decree to allow the Fall — in fact I couldn't even have spelt or pronounced either word).

I continued again: 'Neither was it any faith that God foresaw these persons would place in Christ, because again we have seen the Calvinist belief in man's inability to have faith unless God gives it to him.

'The only basis the Calvinist would allow for the election of this people, in the light of their depravity and inability,' I now stated emphatically, as I saw clearly the connection between the first and second points of Calvinism, 'is the will of God, and the will of God alone. The Calvinist would say that it had to be the will of God, and the will of God alone, for two reasons: first, there was nothing good within any man that would make God choose one over the other; and second, man could not choose God because of his powerlessness. Therefore God did not choose man on any basis of man's ability to choose God.'

I was glad that I was (with Dr Sisk's permission) recording these sessions, because I could never have stated the matter quite like that again.

At this point I showed Dr Sisk a brief outline I had constructed which set out the Calvinistic view of unconditional election.

1. God has a group of people the Bible calls the elect.
2. God has chosen these people to be his own.
3. God chose these people to be his own before the foundation of the world.
4. God has chosen these people to be his own on the basis of his will, and his will alone, and not on the basis of anything he saw, or foresaw in them.

I noted (I'm sure Dr Sisk knew it already) that the real point of separation between Calvinists and others was the fourth statement. Others would agree that God had a group of people who were his own, whom he chose before the foundation of the world, but the real point of separation was the basis of the choice of the elect — whether it was something in the people concerned or the sovereign will (I had read that phrase somewhere) of God alone.

I explained that it is because of this one point that the Calvinist view is called 'unconditional' — because election finds no condition in man for its choice. The condition of choice is completely with God.

Dr Sisk agreed, and then remarked, 'Yes, this is called God's decree of election, and it is certainly based on God's sovereign will and his will alone. Would the Calvinist believe that God's decrees and his sovereignty extend to anything else besides election?'

My answer to that had to be that the Calvinist believed that God has decreed whatever comes to pass.

I anticipated Dr Sisk's next question: 'Does that mean that God has decreed sin?'

I admitted, 'Yes, according to the Calvinist, God has decreed all things, even sin.'

'What,' Dr Sisk then asked, 'would you ask the Calvinist concerning his view of God's predestination and election of all things, including his unconditional choice of a group known as the elect and his predestination of sin?'

I was ready this time. I had spent a few moments jotting down some questions for the Calvinist on this issue of unconditional election. My list went as follows:

1. Doesn't such a view of election (God chooses one over another with no concern for what is in man) leave us with an unjust God?

2. Why didn't God choose all men as the elect if his is the final voice on who is saved and who is not?

3. If we say that God has decreed all things, including sin, are we not making God the author of sin?

Dr Sisk seemed pleased again that our session had gone so well. He complimented me on my thinking, analysis and objectivity in handling the subject matter. We made another appointment for early the next week so we could discuss limited atonement.

The evening went as well as the afternoon discussion period. Todd and I went to the girls' church. Terry did give me encouragement to invite her out, as did the girl Todd was interested in. So we went out for a burger and Coke, and then saw them home.

As we drove back to college after the 'big date' I paid little attention to Todd as he rattled on and on about how this was 'the' girl for him. He said he knew his track record had left a lot of broken hearts along the way, but this girl and this situation were different. She was the girl he was going to marry.

I chuckled under my breath as I found myself thinking the same thing: 'I have just left the girl I am going to marry.' I had little confidence in Todd's conviction, but I was certain about mine.

I laughed again as I thought, 'Yes, of course, that's the girl I'm going to marry! It's been predestined from the foundation of the world!'

Was I beginning to think like a Calvinist?

Whether a Calvinist or not, this night my heart was so smitten with Terry that I hoped at least she had been predestined for my life!

7.
For some or for all?

The glorious euphoria of Wednesday evening carried over through the rest of the week, and it deepened after I rang Terry on Thursday to ask for a date on Friday evening. She accepted with enthusiasm, which encouraged me greatly. Friday evening was about the only time I could take her out because I spent all day Saturday visiting in the area around the church, and then Sunday was busy with two services.

I didn't tell Todd about the arrangement for Friday night because of a fear he would try to muscle in and turn it into a double date. I had to tell him, though, on Friday when he wanted to borrow my car for his date that night. I refused him, and then rejected his offer to make up a foursome, giving him the reason that I wanted us to spend some time by ourselves, getting to know each other, rather than being thrown together in a crowd.

Then he asked me for another five-dollar loan (even though he already owed me twenty). He promised to pay the whole debt on Monday because he was preaching on Sunday and would probably get a cheque, he said. Reluctantly I handed him five dollars, and he chided, 'Maybe we'll see you tonight.' I thought to myself, 'I hope not.'

Before the date on Friday night I had the next appointment with Dr Sisk in the afternoon. He had warned me that the most difficult point of the Calvinistic acrostic was the third one — limited atonement. As I made my way to his office for our time of discussion, I was not as confident on this point as I had been on the others. I really wondered at the time how anyone could believe in a limited atonement, but thought perhaps my reaction against it was because I did not understand what the point said.

'Well, it's limited atonement time today, isn't it?' Dr Sisk said as he greeted me. 'Maybe you can help me on this subject!' he added with a smile.

'Well,' I began with a deep breath and a sigh of relief, which was more for the sake of getting me started than to do anything else, 'I will begin by noting that the doctrine of a limited atonement states that the death of Christ had a particular design and purpose towards the elect, rather than just a general design and purpose towards all men. Am I correct?'

'Yes, but what does that mean?' asked Dr Sisk.

'I think it means that the death of Christ guarantees the salvation of the elect. Since all men are totally depraved, and since God has chosen a people to be his own, God has also provided an atonement for them which guarantees their salvation.'

Dr Sisk winked approvingly.

'The Calvinist would say,' I continued, 'that it is a matter of whether the death of Christ was to make salvation *possible* for all men but guarantee the salvation of no man (the Arminian view), or whether the death of Christ was to make salvation *actual* and guarantee the salvation of all the elect (the Calvinist view).'

'You have stated the Calvinist view correctly,' Dr Sisk commented. 'Now, how does this third point of limited atonement relate to the first two?'

'Actually it follows logically from the first two,' I replied. 'If man is totally depraved, and cannot and does not come to God except on the basis of God's election, then the atonement must be for the elect, or they would not be able to be saved. On the other hand, if there is such a thing as election, and some are not of the elect, then there would be no purpose nor necessity for Christ to die for those who are not elect. The Calvinist would argue that if Christ died for all men in the same manner, then he died for the non-elect too, and then there would be those in hell for whom Christ died. This the Calvinist will not accept. All of those for whom Christ died will be saved. The blood of Christ was not shed in vain for those who will be in hell, the Calvinist would argue.'

I stopped to come up for air. Dr Sisk immediately plunged me under again.

'Oh, so the Calvinist would put a limitation on the power of the death of Christ, would he?' Dr Sisk probed.

I could tell he was playing with me to see if I had correctly understood limited atonement. I didn't fall into the trap.

'The Calvinist would put a limitation on the *design* of the death of Christ—his death was for the elect in a unique way. The Calvinist would not put a limitation on the *power* of the death of Christ. Because Christ was an infinite person, his death has an infinite power. His death, had God so designed, could have atoned for the sins of all men. There is no limitation in the power of the death of Christ. The limitation is in the design of the death of Christ, as set forth by God's eternal decree of election. For this reason, to avoid confusion, some Calvinists would speak of a "particular" atonement rather than a "limited" atonement.'

Dr Sisk was enjoying this, seeing me squirm and sweat as I tried to put the Calvinist position on atonement into words.

He fired another question: 'Would, or could, a Calvinist ever speak of the death of Christ for the non-elect?'

'I found Calvinists disagreeing here,' I continued thoughtfully, trying hard to remember what I had read. 'Some of them speak of the death of Christ as being "sufficient" for all men, even the non-elect. This would emphasize the unlimited power of the death of Christ, even as concerns the non-elect. Others, it seems, don't like that term, perhaps because of a fear that it might indicate a general atonement. All of them seem to like the term "efficient to the elect", which speaks of the design of the death of Christ as relating to the elect only. "Sufficient to all, but efficient to the elect," was a statement I found used by many Calvinists, but not all of them.'

'Well, what's my next question for you?' Dr Sisk asked.

I laughed and rejoined, 'Oh, so you want me to ask the questions now as well as answer them?'

However, it was not hard to guess his next question. What would I ask the Calvinist to explain, as I faced objectively his view of limited atonement?

'I would ask the Calvinist the following questions,' I declared:

1. What about all the Bible verses (John 3:16; 2 Peter 3:9; etc.) which seem to indicate that Christ died for the sins of all the men of the world?

2. Why does the death of Christ have to have a particular design? Why could not God have given it only a general design?

3. Where is a limited, or particular, atonement taught in the Bible?

By this time it was getting late, and we decided to meet again early next week to discuss irresistible grace. As I stepped out into the corridor, I saw Dr Bloom closing the door of his office. When he saw me he insisted that I step inside for a few moments. He was much friendlier than he had been previously.

Perhaps it had dawned on him that I was not the enemy, but a searching student. Perhaps he had gained respect for me because I stood up to him. Perhaps he had heard I was meeting regularly with Dr Sisk. Whatever the case, he gave me a list of books with page numbers and urged me to read those pages noted. I thanked him, assured him I would, and left with him insisting that I get back in touch after I had read the material.

I really wanted to see him again, not so much to discuss Calvinism with him, but to talk to him about his attitude towards Calvinism and Calvinists. I determined that the next visit would be on my terms — when I chose and only after I had thoroughly understood Calvinism, whether I agreed or disagreed with it or not.

The date that evening went really well! I found out we had a lot in common. Besides that, she was a spiritual girl, who had committed her life to the Lord's service. She was willing to do with her life whatever the Lord wanted.

She smiled when I teased her and asked what that might include.

'Oh, a missionary, maybe, or a teacher. Or maybe a church secretary.' Then my heart almost stopped as she added, 'Who knows? Maybe I might even be a preacher's wife some day!'

8.
Amazing grace!

I didn't know exactly how to understand it or to explain it, but something unusual was taking place in Lime Creek Baptist Church as I was ministering there in my fourth month as pastor. We were working and praying for a great outpouring of God's Spirit, and I thought I saw evidences of such a movement beginning to be manifested in our midst.

For one thing, God's people had come to have a real burden for prayer, and morning prayer meetings through the week had broken out besides the usual times of prayer.

For another thing, people had begun to confess sin. Many of them had even gone to the former pastor and apologized for their attitudes and feelings towards him, and for the unkind words they had spoken to him and about him. It didn't seem to matter that he had been wrong too. They could only see their own sin, and wanted God's cleansing and forgiveness.

I had hoped such actions would have brought about some kind of humbling on his part too, but they hadn't. When I ran into him one day in the community, he said, 'It's a good thing those folk over in your church are getting right with God and apologizing to me. If they hadn't, I'm afraid God might have had to deal harshly with some of them! There are still some others who need to humble themselves and confess their sin.'

Poor fellow! He couldn't see any wrongdoing on his own part in the break of fellowship in the church. I wondered, 'Are all Calvinists like this man?'

The next appointment with Dr Sisk was on Tuesday afternoon. About thirty minutes before going to his office I sprawled out on the bed in my room to go over the notes from the reading. I had to be honest. I was having trouble with irresistible grace.

As I sighed and moaned and squirmed and got up from time to time to pace the floor, it even interrupted Todd's reading.

'What's wrong with you?' he asked. 'Did Terry turn you down for Friday night?'

Poor old Todd! The only problem he could ever foresee in life had to concern a girl.

'No,' I said, 'I'm wrestling with a theological problem.'

'Oh, well bounce it off me. Maybe I can help you,' he offered.

'Have you ever heard of irresistible grace?' I queried.

'Of course,' said Todd seriously. 'She's the girl I dated last summer in New Orleans,' with which he burst out laughing and left the room.

As I made my way to Dr Sisk's office, still thinking of Todd's answer, I found myself amazed at the different ways people reacted to avoid any possibility of theological discussion.

I could very easily have resisted the subject of irresistible grace, both in consideration of the subject matter itself, and of the difficulties it presented. But I had set out on this journey, and I was not about to turn back. Everyone I had met along the way, those who knew nothing and those who thought they knew everything, those who hated the subject and those who were indifferent, only drove me on!

So it was with great uncertainty that I began my definition in Dr Sisk's office that Tuesday afternoon: 'The doctrine of irresistible grace' (at least I had made a beginning) 'must be seen in its relationship to the first three points of the Calvinistic acrostic.

'If man is totally depraved, and therefore cannot come to God in his own strength; and if man has been unconditionally chosen to be one of God's elect; and if the atonement of Christ is designed for these elect and guarantees their salvation; then it logically follows that the elect will be saved. They will be irresistibly called and drawn to Christ.'

I looked up at Dr Sisk rather puzzled.

'Well, what's the problem, then?' he asked.

'It's not a question of just one problem,' I replied. 'There's any number of problems!' I sensed I was losing my objectivity. 'Well, let me put it this way,' I added, calming down a little, 'that leaves me with several questions I would ask the Calvinist.'

1. What if a person wants to come to Christ for salvation, and he is not one of the elect, and irresistible grace does not call him? Does that mean he cannot be saved?

2. What if one of the elect does not want to come to Christ for salvation, but irresistible grace calls him? Does that mean that God drags him over the doorstep of salvation as he screams and shouts his rebellion against God?

3. What will such a doctrine do to evangelism and missions? If God is going to draw the elect irresistibly, will not that undercut the responsibility of men to repent and believe the gospel, and also the responsibility of the church to carry the gospel to all the world?

4. Does not such a view violate man's free agency and free will?

It was obvious that Dr Sisk could have given the Calvinist answers to my questions, but he did not. He only replied, 'Well, you have much to think about in the days ahead, haven't you?'

'One other thing,' I added, when I saw he would give me no help. 'Some Calvinists prefer the term "efficacious grace" to "irresistible grace" because they no doubt think it may take some of the sting out of the latter term.'

We made another appointment for Friday to discuss the last point of the acrostic — the perseverance of the saints. I left his office almost fully convinced that I could never be a Calvinist. I was convinced, however, that I would continue to study the position so I could refute any Calvinist I might encounter, rather than simply reacting emotionally to him by calling him an idiot and his position heresy.

When back in my room, I recorded the fruit of the conversation in my notebook. It was beginning to bulge now. I thought I would probably have to get a bigger one before the search was over, as I was accumulating a number of areas for further research and study.

Todd had gone off somewhere, so I turned out the light in the room and stretched out on the bed to rest for a few moments. I couldn't help but think of how God had saved me.

As I thought of what I was before I was saved, and how far away from him I had been, I wondered, 'Had my salvation come by irresistible grace? Had my salvation come because God had chosen me to be one of his elect from the foundation of the world? Could I have been completely left out of God's plan of salvation?'

A strange sensation came over me. I began to weep. Was this what John Newton meant by his song, 'Amazing grace, how sweet the sound, that saved a wretch like me!'?

9.
Keeping on to the end

I looked forward to the next Friday for two reasons — the discussion with Dr Sisk and, obviously, the date with Terry. Friday would be a good day — or so I thought.

I wasn't ready for what took place on Friday morning. I don't suppose there is any way you could get ready for such an event. I was called out of one of my lectures and told to phone the chairman of my deacons at the church. He informed me that the evening before one of our choice and most committed young men had been killed in a road accident.

The boy who was killed was just eighteen years old, and was looking forward to leaving high school in June. He had been hit by a drunken driver on his way home from a school basketball match the night before. The family wanted me to come immediately.

As I ministered to the boy's family and the church family that weekend, and as I preached at the funeral (my first one — and what a tough one it was for a first one!), I kept wondering about the Calvinist view that God had decreed all things. Had he, or even could he, have decreed this? If he had, how could he have done so? If he hadn't, had something happened outside of his will? Had Satan produced something that God could not have stopped? That thought was frightening! Or had something happened which God could have stopped, but he didn't for reasons beyond our understanding? Either way, the explanations were not without difficulty.

On Sunday the Lord seemed to use this event to deepen the spirit of revival developing in the church. Many committed their lives afresh to the Lord, and several young people even made professions of faith. Though I wanted the Lord to have his way, I was also careful not to do anything to produce false decisions which would be made only in the light of the event of the previous week without serious thought and understanding. These professions of faith, however, in the weeks that followed, did prove to be of the Lord.

One other positive thing came out of the weekend — Terry came to the funeral service, and I was able to introduce her to my congregation. She was a great encouragement to me as I sought to minister the Word that day.

The unexpected events of that week and weekend forced us to postpone the planned Friday meeting with Dr Sisk. We rescheduled it for the following Tuesday.

Honestly, I was glad we had just one more meeting on the Calvinistic acrostic. I knew it would be several weeks, even a month or so, before another meeting, because I would need time for further research as I tackled the next step. As I entered Dr Sisk's office, I was still working on the basis of the study and reading done over the Christmas holidays.

I began the discussion with an attempt to define the Calvinistic doctrine of the perseverance of the saints. I said, 'Like the other points of the Calvinistic acrostic, the doctrine of perseverance stems from, and is the logical conclusion of, the previous points. If the others are true, then so is perseverance, so says the Calvinist.'

I paused for Dr Sisk's reaction. 'Elaborate on that!' he promptly said.

'Well, if man is totally depraved and cannot do anything to help himself spiritually; and if God is absolutely sovereign in the matter of election, choosing the elect on the basis of his will, and his will alone; and if Christ's death was for the elect, guaranteeing their salvation; and if God calls the elect irresistibly — then does it not follow that God will ensure the final salvation of these elect, that is, they will persevere to the final end?'

Dr Sisk nodded his usual agreement with my definition. He laughed and teasing me suggested, 'Try saying that again!'

I told him I probably couldn't say it again in the same way, but I would put it another way: 'If the elect did not persevere, then the eternal election of God would fail, and this the Calvinist could not admit. If God decrees something, it will come to pass, including the final salvation of the elect.

'Or again,' I suggested, 'if the elect did not persevere, then the death of Christ would be a failure, because its design was to guarantee their salvation.

'Or even further,' I concluded, 'if the elect did not persevere, then the grace of God could be resisted by the saved, since they could reject it in a final manner *after* they were saved, even though grace was irresistible *before* they were saved.'

'You've said a lot,' Dr Sisk admitted, 'and it's the Calvinistic position. But you haven't defined the doctrine yet!'

Apologetically I offered a definition: 'Perseverance is the doctrine which says that those who are the elect, because they have been the object of God's eternal decree of election and of Christ's atonement, shall continue in the way of salvation, as the same power of God that saved them will also keep them and sanctify them unto their final salvation.'

'Does this rule out backsliding?' Dr Sisk asked.

'No, it doesn't, but it rules out the possibility that someone can profess to be a Christian and yet live in a supposedly backslidden state for a number of years without facing the chastening hand of God. Backsliding will occur among Christians, but the doctrine of perseverance says the true believer will not remain there endlessly. If someone does, he had better put a big question mark beside his profession of faith.'

'What does this doctrine do to the "carnal Christian" idea?' Dr Sisk asked.

'What's a "carnal Christian"?' I asked. I had never heard of the term.

Dr Sisk came to my aid: 'A "carnal Christian", according to some, is someone who has been truly saved, yet lives as if he is lost. He has made a profession of faith, and maybe lived like a Christian for a while. But now he has gone back to the world, and both those around him in the world and those in the church wouldn't know he was a Christian. Only God knows his heart. He spends the rest of his life in this condition, but because of his salvation experience, he will be in eternity with Christ. He is carnal, but he is a Christian. Or he is a Christian, but he is carnal.'

'Well, I don't think the Calvinist would like that viewpoint!' I told him. 'The Calvinist would say, if there is no perseverance there is no salvation, and if there is salvation, there will be perseverance.'

'One more question,' Dr Sisk said, 'before I let you ask my final question. Is this the same as the usual Baptist definition of "Once saved, always saved"?'

I had never thought of that! Immediately I saw it was not. I countered: 'The Baptist concept of "Once saved, always saved" is only half the coin, and with only half of the coin it seems to me it can become a dangerous doctrine.'

Dr Sisk said nothing, but his face said, 'Explain what you mean,' so I continued: 'The doctrine of perseverance, according to the Calvinist, has two sides — security and perseverance. Yet one cannot exist without the other. The Baptist doctrine of eternal security ("Once saved, always saved"), overlooks or neglects the necessity of perseverance as the proof of true salvation. Thus by telling a person of eternal security without telling him of the reality of perseverance as the proof of salvation, one could produce the same results as the "carnal Christian" doctrine — people who think they are saved but who are not. The doctrine of eternal security without the other side of the coin becomes a licence to sin for those who have merely professed faith in Christ, but who have never truly been saved. The Calvinist doctrine of perseverance gives both comfort to the believer (he is eternally secure) and reality to his profession (he realizes the proof of his salvation is a perseverance in the Christian life).'

When Dr Sisk asked me for questions I would put to the Calvinist at this point, I honestly told him I didn't have any. Though I was still wrestling with the first four points, this one made sense and seemed to be thoroughly scriptural.

After a few more comments, I told him I would need more time for study before we could meet again and, with the college work and my responsibilities at church, I wasn't sure when that would be possible.

10.
The search continues

Very soon after my last meeting with Dr Sisk, I set aside a couple of hours to summarize the search as it had unfolded thus far. I felt this was necessary in case I forgot or missed some important point which had already been unearthed, or some topic which I needed to pursue in the future.

I began by attempting to define briefly the five points of Calvinism. The first page in the summary section of my notebook read as follows:

Definitions of the five points of Calvinism

1. *Total depravity* is the doctrine which speaks of man's *nature*, and not his *actions*, and it says that he is powerless in his own being to know God, or to come to God.

2. *Unconditional election* states that God chose a people (the elect) from the foundation of the world to be his own, and his choice was on the basis of his sovereign will alone. Therefore, his choosing of the elect was due to no condition or state in man, either known by him, or foreseen by him as he viewed the unfolding of history.

3. *Limited atonement* states that Christ's death was designed to guarantee the salvation of the elect, and therefore this death, though in its *power* it was sufficient for all men, yet in its *design* it applied only to the elect.

4. *Irresistible grace* states that God will irresistibly call the elect unto himself through the preaching of the gospel of Jesus Christ, and by that call the decree of election will be fulfilled and the particular purpose of the atonement will be applied.

5. *Perseverance of the saints* states that the elect are not only secure for eternity, but the proof of their election and the evidence of their security are the continuing work of sanctification within them which causes them to persevere in the Christian life.

On the following page, I made a list of areas for further research.

Areas for further research

1. *Biblical* study needed to determine if these five points of Calvinism will stand the test of Scripture.

2. *Historical* study needed to seek to understand if Baptists were Calvinists in their past history, and if they left Calvinism, when and why that took place.

3. *Contemporary* study of current Calvinist writers (or even others) to seek to understand what is the difference between a Calvinist and a hyper-Calvinist.

4. *Theological* study (in all fairness to the Calvinist) to seek to understand how he would answer major objections to the Calvinist position, many of which I stated in my discussions with Dr Sisk.

I further made note of several other observations and conclusions I had realized during the course of the study.

Other observations

1. Most Christians are quite ignorant of the true definition of Calvinism, yet speak freely and confidently as they attempt to define it and refute it.

2. Many Christians find it very difficult to speak of Calvinism without becoming very subjective and emotional.

3. Some Calvinists are offensive to other members of the body of Christ as they seek to promote their beliefs. Perhaps this is not always the Calvinist's fault, but at times it appears to have been due to his attitude and methods.

4. Some Calvinists seem to be more concerned to make 'new Calvinists' than 'new converts'.

5. Some Calvinists use what appear to be Arminian tactics to promote their Calvinism, which would be the height of contradiction.

My next question was not which area to pursue, but how I could find time in my busy schedule to do any study on the areas where research was needed.

Then I had a stroke of genius! Why not write a paper for one of my classes on some subject I needed to research? That way I could kill two birds with one stone. I could meet the requirement of the course for a paper, and I could pursue some aspect of my research.

But which subject for which course was the question? How many classes does one take which would allow me honestly to make an in-depth study of one of the subjects confronting me in my search?

As I analysed the situation, I decided there was only one class which would allow me to carry out my plan — a church history class. But guess what? Dr Bloom taught that class. Would it not be inviting disaster to do such a thing, especially after my earlier confrontation with him?

I could write a paper on Calvinism in Baptist history, and could answer several questions: 'Were Baptists strongly Calvinistic in their history? If so, who were the strong Calvinist Baptist preachers, theologians and writers? What about the Baptist confessions of faith — were they Calvinistic? How and why did Baptists leave Calvinism? When did Baptists leave Calvinism?'

I really got excited over the possibilities. But would I dare, in the light of Dr Bloom's animosity towards Calvinism?

Quickly I began to calculate what kind of a final grade I would get in that church history class even if Dr Bloom gave me an 'F' on my paper. When I finally concluded that the very worst I could get for the course as a whole under the most horrible of circumstances would be a 'C+', I decided to risk it. After all, he couldn't be any more annoyed than he was the first time I talked to him about the subject.

Thus the plan was set! Now, I threw my whole being, while on campus, into that paper. It wouldn't be wise to turn in a half-hearted, sloppy piece of work on this paper. It had to be quality all round!

Though I was busy that whole month with the paper, it didn't stop the development of the other pursuit. Terry and I did manage to spend some time together, and when I really couldn't find the time, I was encouraged to know that she understood.

I hadn't yet approached her with the subject of Calvinism. I wasn't sure whether she would have a theological mind or not. Besides that, what if her church had faced some bad experiences with a Calvinist or Calvinism? What if her pastor was strongly opposed to Calvinism?

True, I was not a Calvinist, but people were so emotional about the subject, that even if you wanted to talk about it or discuss it, some had a tendency to write you off as either being a Calvinist or a Calvinist sympathizer.

I knew some time soon I would have to talk to her about the matter, but the time was not yet ripe. Maybe one way would be for her to type my paper for me. That would introduce her to the subject. She had offered her services previously. Why not take her up on it? It would certainly help me in another way — I was hopeless as a typist and this was one time when I definitely did not want to hand in a blotched, wrinkled, crumpled manuscript covered in corrections.

Also during this period, the revival at the church continued! Crowds began to gather of unusual proportions. Something was taking place which I did not understand, and which I was not producing. God was at work. All admitted it and no one dared deny it. I had no idea of what was yet to come in the life of that little church!

11.
Roots in history

As I began my study of Calvinism in Baptist history, I made no claim to any knowledge of the subject, let alone to being an expert in that area. But what I learned convinced me that most Baptists (even preachers) knew little more than I did about the matter. I was shocked as the data began to unfold!

My research centred on several key questions, which I sought to answer one at a time. Were Baptists in their early history ever Calvinists? If so, when and why did Baptists lose their Calvinism? Who were some of the great Baptist Calvinists?

1. Were Baptists ever Calvinists?

I soon found the answer to this first question. I discovered that modern Baptists traced their heritage to the early English Baptists of the Reformation period. These early forerunners were divided into two groups — the General Baptists and the Particular Baptists. The General Baptists were not as Calvinistic as the others, and certainly did not believe in a particular atonement. They believed in a general atonement, that is, that the death of Christ had a general design towards all men. The Particular Baptists, as their name implies, believed in a limited, or particular, atonement.

Second, I discovered that these Particular Baptists of the seventeenth century were the more influential of the two groups. Their Calvinism was reflected in two confessions of faith, the *First London Confession* of 1644 and the *Second London Confession* of 1689.

I found strong and clear statements on election in each of them. The *First London Confession* of 1644 stated:

'And touching his creature man, God had in Christ before the foundation of the world, according to the good pleasure of his will, foreordained some men to eternal life through Jesus Christ, to the praise and glory of his grace, leaving the rest in their sin to their just condemnation, to the praise of his justice.'

The *Second London Confession* of 1689 further elaborated the point:

'By the decree of God, for the manifestation of his glory some men and angels are predestined, or foreordained to eternal life, through Jesus Christ, to the praise of his glorious grace; others being left to act in their sin to their just condemnation, to the praise of his glorious justice.

'These angels and men thus predestinated and foreordained are particularly and unchangeably designed, and their number so certain and definite that it cannot be either increased or diminished.

'Those of mankind that are predestinated to life, God, before the foundation of the world was laid, according to his eternal and immutable purpose, and the secret counsel and good pleasure of his will, hath chosen in Christ unto everlasting glory, out of his mere free grace and love; without any other thing in the creature as a condition or cause moving him thereunto.'

Beyond even English history, I found that Baptists in early America shared the same viewpoint, as evidenced in their greatest confession of faith, the *Philadelphia Confession of Faith*. In fact, this confession was pretty much a reproduction of the *Second London Confession,* except that it contained a few extra categories. But as far as the subject of divine election was concerned, it read exactly the same.

The widespread influence of this *Philadelphia Confession* was confirmed by a statement I found in one very reliable source that 'Throughout the South it shaped Baptist thought generally and has perhaps been the most influential of all confessions.'[1]

Thus the question, 'Were Baptists in their early history ever Calvinists?' had to be answered with a strong and definite 'Yes!'

2. When and why did Baptists lose their Calvinism?

It seemed to me that these two questions were so closely related that if I discovered the one I would also uncover the other. But the answer to these two questions was not easy to find.

Finally, after pouring over dozens of books on Baptist history, and after giving it much thought and meditation, I was convinced I had uncovered the answer. Even then it could not be stated in a short and simple manner. But none the less, I tried to state it in summary fashion as follows: Baptists lost their Calvinism some time in the past one hundred years due to the influence of the two Great Awakenings and the events which accompanied them.

To elaborate, Baptists were strong Calvinists in their early history in America, as was shown by the *Philadelphia Confession of Faith*, already mentioned. This confession would have to be dated in the early part of the eighteenth century, perhaps about 1725.

When the First Great Awakening of 1740 (which, by the way, was a Calvinistic movement) exploded on the scene of early American history, Baptists were not involved in it. Baptists became involved in it as members of the established churches, who had experienced revival and renewal, left to join Baptist churches. These individuals were known as 'Separates', and they brought to the Baptist churches the spirit of the awakening, which was good, but they also brought some dangerous tendencies, including a distrust of the established clergy and a view of the immediate illumination of the Holy Spirit.

The excesses of this First Great Awakening were dangerous and damaging to Baptist life in America. Baptists began to move in the direction of an anti-theological, or non-theological spirit in their attitudes and thinking. They became very pietistic, with strong appeal to the emotions. They came to undervalue ministerial education. They became somewhat anti-educational and anti-historical. They began to fear creeds and confessions of faith. Up to this time confessions of faith and even catechisms had been used by Baptists without question or apology.

When the Second Great Awakening of about 1830 struck, Baptists were already in the process of rethinking some of their beliefs, with a modified Calvinism beginning to develop. Though Calvinism was still very strong, other tendencies, which were to become a further threat to the remaining influence of Calvinism, continued to grow and multiply. Pietism was primary, while doctrine was relegated to a secondary position.There came to be a much greater emphasis on the life of the individual, as opposed to corporate concerns being primary. A strong opposition to confessions developed.

This is not to say that Baptists fled their Calvinistic heritage at this point of history; but it is to say that some tendencies — not all of them bad — began to develop which, if carried to an extreme, could become very detrimental to their doctrinal heritage.

To summarize, the Calvinism of Baptists was under constant and direct attack in the eighteenth and nineteenth centuries, first from the revivalism of the Separates, then by Methodist Arminianism, and also from the Free Will Baptist movement, and finally from Charles G. Finney. Having embraced revivalism and its tendencies after the First Great Awakening, and having been suddenly vaulted to great prominence and influence among the people and the religious scene in America, Baptists were very interested in maintaining their newly acquired position of religious leadership and in keeping their movement growing.

As time wore on, the remnants of their Calvinism were still strong in some places, though modified. But even that amount of Calvinism became more difficult to defend before the simple, uneducated, common-sense man, or even the rational, educated, philosophically trained man. Instead of continuing to hold and defend their Calvinistic theology, they strained their Calvinistic theological framework to accommodate the new religious mood of the day.

The change was slow, and Calvinism continued to be held and defended by some even into the twentieth century. But by the middle of that century, Calvinism was all but dead among Baptists, except for a weakened definition of the fifth point. Baptists of past history called the fifth point 'the perseverance of the saints'. Baptists of the middle years of the twentieth century call it 'the eternal security of the believer'.

One final point must be made. Some time just past the middle of the twentieth century, a revival of Calvinism among Baptists began, and it appears to be continuing and growing today.

Who were some of the great Baptist Calvinists?

This was not a difficult question to answer. History abounds with great Baptists who were Calvinists. The following is a partial list:

1. Isaac Backus, New England Baptist, born 1724.
2. John Leland, New England Baptist, born 1754.
3. James P. Boyce, founder and first president of Southern Baptist Theological Seminary in Louisville, Kentucky.
4. J. L. Dagg, an early Southern Baptist theologian.
5. P. M. Mell, president of the Southern Baptist Convention for seventeen years, longer than any other president ever served.
6. Adoniram Judson, born 1788, the first foreign missionary to go forth from the United States.
7. Charles H. Spurgeon, the great English preacher and pastor of the nineteenth century.

The above facts, plus other details, composed the content of the paper I wrote and handed in to Dr Bloom. Full documentation was given. Knowing that this was one professor who marked and returned papers quickly, I waited with great anxiety for my paper to return.

How terrified I was, when instead of a returned and marked paper like all the other students, I found a note in my mailbox to make an appointment with Dr Bloom for the purpose of discussing my paper and its content!

The time had come! I could not pick the hour of confrontation now (if that was what he intended). I made an appointment, putting it off at least for a week and almost wishing I hadn't gone to him originally at the outset of the search.

Whether I believed in predestination or not, my future was set. Before the term was over, I had to keep that appointment, whatever it held!

1. *Encyclopedia of Southern Baptists,* vol. I, p.308.

12.
A dreaded interview

It was a cold and blustery March day when I made my way across campus for the meeting with Dr Bloom. I had no idea what to expect. I had sought to anticipate any questions he might ask, and was as thoroughly prepared as possible.

In planning a course of action, I had decided to let him talk. He had called me for the meeting, and he would have to initiate the conversation. I would answer in as polite a manner as possible, but also with as few words as possible. I would be open to the possibility of asking him questions, thus turning the focus upon him rather than on myself. Finally, if I had the opportunity, I was going to mention his unloving attitude towards Calvinists, which I thought was unscriptural.

As I analysed the situation, there was no way he could legitimately nail me. I had fulfilled the assignment. The research was beyond question. The English mechanics of the paper were impeccable (thanks to Terry). The college must allow me the academic freedom to write my conclusions, and the professors should be open enough to judge the paper on its academic merits even if they disagreed with the viewpoint.

Thus with a measure of fearful confidence, I knocked on Dr Bloom's door. His usual sombre and serious, 'Come in!' greeted me.

'Have a seat,' he said, motioning me to a chair, but hardly looking up. And then my wait began, as he was true to his usual practice of keeping the student waiting, while he finished what he was doing.

I vowed as I waited that if I ever taught, I would never treat a student in that manner.

Finally, he turned away from his desk and spoke. I listened for hints not only in his words, but also in the tone of his voice, or in his actions or manners, which might give me some clue to his attitude towards my paper. But he was stoic as he observed, 'Mr Pointer, you have written a very interesting paper.'

As he spoke he had my paper in his lap and was thumbing through it. I could see he had used his pencil profusely in making comments in the margins, but I couldn't read any of them because they were upside down from where I was sitting. I was dying to see what he had written!

I wondered to myself, 'Does he realize what he is putting me through? Is this procedure on purpose, or is he totally insensitive to the student's feelings in this kind of setting?' How much more fair and proper it would have been for him to have sent my paper back to me through the mail, let me read it, along with his comments, and then meet with him!

If he was hoping to invoke conversation from me by his first remark, he failed. I said nothing. There was no proper reply I could give to that kind of statement. Thus there was a period of silence.

Finally he spoke again. He asked bluntly, 'Mr Pointer, are you a Calvinist?'

My answer was according to my plan, short and to the point., as I declared simply, 'No sir.' I felt no compulsion to say anything more, as long as he kept me in the dark as to his motive and purpose for the meeting.

Silence prevailed again for a few moments, as the intellectual battle of wits continued.

'Do you think you could ever be a Calvinist?' he finally asked.

I wondered to myself what kind of question that was. I answered, 'Well, sir, that depends.'

'On what?' he shot back, evidently thinking we were now getting somewhere in the conversation.

'Let me put it this way, sir. Forgetting Calvinism for a moment, I stand before you and honestly declare that if I ever become convinced that Scripture teaches a position, I will believe it. Though I will examine many theological beliefs in the years to come, my method will not be to rule them out, as I first face them, because of some preconceived prejudice or bias towards them. Rather, I shall first of all seek objectively to understand them, and then examine them in the light of Scripture. At the present, I am seeking to understand Calvinism objectively, and then I will examine its beliefs in the light of Scripture to determine if I agree or disagree with their tenets. I accept this as the method of scholarship, and would label any other approach as prejudiced and doomed because of human presuppositions.'

As I closed that lengthy statement, I was inwardly amazed. Had that long dissertation come out of my mouth? I, who had intended to speak briefly, had rattled on that long?

My answer seemed to startle Dr Bloom also. For the first time in his life I saw him speechless, as he cleared his throat and thumbed quickly through my paper once again.

I plucked up my courage and spoke again: 'Furthermore, sir, if, on the one hand, I ever reject Calvinism, I will still recognize those who hold that position as brothers in Christ. I have already come to see that there are some Calvinists who are unbalanced in their views, but I will refuse to castigate all Calvinists of past history, or all Calvinists of present history, on the basis of the extremes of some of that group. My paper has shown that for a Baptist to be a Calvinist is not heretical. Neither would I label Baptists today who are Calvinists as heretical.

'If, on the other hand, I become a Calvinist out of a conviction that this is what Scripture teaches, I would continue to recognize Christians who are not Calvinists as brothers in the Lord and as members of the body of Christ, and I would seek to help my Calvinist brothers who I feel have become unbalanced in their views to a better understanding of Calvinism.'

When I had finished these words I braced myself for his response. Had I said too much? Had I sounded pompous and proud as I had spoken? That had not been my intention.

At this point Dr Bloom turned to my paper. He said, 'Actually, Mr Pointer, there is only one thing I can find wrong with your paper. You didn't give your view in it.'

I thought to myself that this was a flimsy reason to call me into his office. Of all the problems other students had in their papers, why waste time with someone who had erred at this small point?

Not trying to sound defensive, still I turned the tables on him. I stated matter of factly but humbly, 'Sir, I wasn't aware that a research paper required me to give my opinion. I thought you would be more interested in the academic and objective study of a question or subject, and the objective conclusions stemming from that research, than in my opinions and ideas. In fact, I remember that the first paper I wrote for you in my first year, you told me to stick with the objective facts and conclusions, and not to be so opinionated in the discussion. I will accept your critique at this point, but I would really be more concerned for you to tell me if I had erred in my research and in the stating of the objective facts of history concerning Baptists and Calvinists.'

'No, no, no no!' he muttered. 'You haven't erred in your dealing with Baptist history. You are correct. Baptists were strong Calvinists in their early history. But can't you see that Baptists are better off today not being Calvinists than they were back there in history as Calvinists?'

I was tempted to ask, 'In what way are Baptists better off today not being Calvinists?' I rejected that possible reply, and instead countered with what I supposed he would have given as an answer to my question had I put it.

'I'm not so sure Baptists are better off today as they embrace non-Calvinist views than they were when they were Calvinists. If one wishes to cite a greater evangelistic and missionary concern, one would have to admit that some of the greatest evangelistic preachers and some of the greatest Baptist missionaries were Calvinists. One would also have to admit, at least I would, that the modern-day non-Calvinistic Baptists have some problems of their own that Calvinistic Baptists did not have.'

'What problems?' he immediately snapped.

'Well, modern-day Baptists have the problem of the infiltration of liberalism into their denominations. They have a church purity problem. They have a great problem of non-resident church membership. They are not as doctrinally informed as Baptists of the past.'

'But surely you don't trace these problems to the matter of Calvinism, do you?' he said, almost laughing.

I replied as honestly as I could: 'I really don't know, sir. I would like to look into that question some day. But for now I am simply pointing out that Baptists of the present, as non-Calvinists, are not without their problems. And those problems seem to be mounting. Maybe there is a connection. I don't know. I only ask that we should not castigate Baptist Calvinists of the past because some problems may have existed in their day. I also ask that we should recognize that modern-day Baptists, as non-Calvinists, have a set of problems of their own which may be related to the change which took place in their theology.'

Finally what I had feared took place! Dr Bloom lost his temper. 'I can see we are wasting our time talking about this matter. I was only trying to help you, but your mind is set and it is clear you will not listen to older counsel and guidance. Let me warn you, young man, that your tendency and sympathy towards Calvinism is dangerous. You can expect that such an attitude will hinder your career in our denomination. If anyone ever asks me for a recommendation regarding your doctrine or ministry, I will have to give them warning that you have some frightening tendencies in your theology.'

With this statement, he handed me my paper and dismissed me.

I was relieved but saddened as I trudged through the newly fallen snow which had accumulated while I was in Dr Bloom's office. One always searches one's own heart after an outburst like that to see if there was any wrongdoing on one's own part. Had I said too much? Had I said something disrespectful? Or maybe it was just Dr Bloom's manner to be blunt and direct and he didn't mean to be so offensive.

Whatever the case, I could hardly believe my eyes, and felt even less inclined to be offended by Dr Bloom, when I opened my paper and found a bright big letter 'A' on the back page! I was encouraged to know that even though he might find fault with my 'dangerous tendencies' (as he put it), he could find no fault with my research.

This convinced me — it is not heresy for a Baptist to be a Calvinist!

13.
Two exciting developments

I didn't have much time to think further about that angry scene in Dr
Bloom's office. Two other explosive situations in my life at this time
occupied all my attention. One was the outbreak at the church of
spiritual revival and renewal — the opposite of what takes place in
most Baptist churches. The second was the romantic blossoming of
the relationship with Terry!

The revival in the church was beyond all human explanation.
Christians continued to be deepened in their commitment and walk
with Christ. There was a developing hunger for the Word of God,
both in their personal lives and from the pulpit. There was a growing
spirit of prayer, with people now concerned to glorify God by doing
his will rather than their own. Even unconverted people from the
local community began to attend the preaching services — something uncommon in our day and our area. I was informed that in the
past decade or so it had been difficult, if not impossible, to get the
lost to attend the church, even during special services such as
missions or evangelistic services.

At times, as word spread of what God was doing, other preachers
asked what method, or methods, I was using to stir up and promote
the renewal. At first I tried to give some explanation, because
everyone seemed to expect it. Finally, I simply would reply, 'It is the
work of God!' However, I found this was too simplistic for some —
they just knew I must have developed a new programme, or a plan
of church growth or renewal, and was being secretive and proud in
not sharing it with them!

The other explosive situation (the developing relationship with Terry) came to a head one evening, but not in the manner most people would believe or expect. The several months of going out together had convinced us that we had a lot in common, and that it seemed the Lord was leading us together — even towards marriage. However, I had not asked her the important question — yet. Todd had kept pushing me (he was not only ecstatic whenever he got engaged himself, but got some kind of excitement by identification when someone he knew reached that important point of progress in a relationship).

But I had not asked her to marry me (though I thought she expected it), because I had never discussed theology with her in great depth. I kept wondering what would happen in the months to come if I came to the conclusion that I was a Calvinist, and found myself engaged to a girl who was not? I knew she was not one of these girls without a thought in her head when it came to theology (like a few I had known and dated), but still I was not sure how open she would be to the doctrine of Calvinism. I had agonized for several weeks as to the best way to find out the answer to this question. What if I broached the subject and the issue became heated? What if she had a closed mind like Dr Bloom? True, she had typed my paper for his class, but it had been presented in a very objective manner, with no hint that I might be leaning in that direction. Actually, I wasn't really leaning that way yet, but sometimes an apparent interest in, or seeming occupation with, a subject is misinterpreted as a belief in it, or a leaning towards it.

My concern over the matter was resolved when, unexpectedly, and much to my surprise, on one of our Friday evening dates she asked me what I thought of Calvinism. Evidently she had picked up the term and some understanding of it through typing my paper. Well, now the subject was out in the open! She had brought it up! The only thing I could do was to tell her honestly and openly my heart.

I didn't arrive back at the hall of residence that Friday evening till about 2 a.m. We spent almost four hours discussing Calvinism! I told her what had stirred my interest in the subject and I explained to her that I had come to no conclusions as to whether I was or was not a Calvinist. I shared with her that I was trying to understand the position objectively. I went over the five points one by one, even stating from memory the objections to each point. She asked me if I would also discuss with her my further thoughts and struggles in the matter — both my conclusions and objections as they grew or were resolved.

I returned to my room in a state of exhilaration over the way the evening had unfolded — especially when it ended with a proposal of marriage being accepted.

14.
Calls from other churches

If excitement and a busy schedule, accompanied by continuous explosive situations, make someone a candidate for a heart attack, I must have been in the running for one in March of 1971. Tabulate into a philosophical or psychological adding machine the encounter with Dr Bloom, the engagement to Terry, the continuation of the search, and the work of the Lord in the church, and the machine might well have blown up! But when someone is busy and rejoicing in the Lord, these possibilities never enter the mind.

The climax to the church situation came when the deacons asked me to preach at their spring mission — a week of special services when the church met each evening around a service of singing and preaching the Word of God. I had never led a mission, but that didn't stop me from jumping at the opportunity. I had always wanted to do so, even though I didn't possess a stock of sermons to rely on for the week. I must admit, I wondered where I would find six or seven extra sermons — all to be preached in one week. But I accepted the challenge, trusting that the God who supplied two sermons a week to a feeble beginner could also as easily supply six or seven. The whole week would be a time of faith and trust in his power, not only for the sermons, but also for whatever results he desired to give.

As always, God did not disappoint us. The church building was packed to overflowing for each service, and the final two services defy my ability to describe them. The Spirit of God came down in such power that I was reminded of the descriptions I had read of the great movements of the past. Professing church members were converted! Drunkards and loose-livers came to Christ! In the final service alone, there was weeping and confession of sin in the middle of my sermon. I could hardly believe it.

In the days that followed, the new converts gave evidence of true salvation, as they were instructed and grounded in the faith. The only disappointing aspect of the meeting was the presence of Jim Mitchell, the former pastor, in the final service, and his boast afterwards that his ministry had been responsible for the great movement of God in our midst. I guess that was better than if he had called it a work of the devil, but at this point I felt a very definite necessity to give all the glory and praise for what had happened to God alone, who had stated in his Word that he would not share his glory with another! I knew that I had not produced these powerful spiritual results, and that no other man could have done either!

One surprising and unexpected development following from the mission was that I began to get phone-calls and contacts of various sorts from pulpit committees of other churches. No such group had ever shown any interest in me, except the folk at Lime Creek Baptist before they called me as pastor. But it was now commonplace for representatives of one or two churches to visit our services each week, and try to arrange a time of discussion with me. I was reluctant to meet with any of them, asking them to give me time to pray about the whole matter. If God had not led them to someone else within a period of six months, and I was still on their hearts, I suggested they should contact me then. Most were not interested in waiting six months, and proceeded to call another man.

One church, however, would not take 'No' for an answer, and this was the most surprising of all. The First Baptist Church of Collegetown (the town where my college was located) contacted me again and again. The church had a large and comfortable building which seated close to a thousand, and in the past had been a leading church in the state. But in recent years they had fallen upon hard times, with only about fifty or so still attending. Their committee came to hear me preach time and time again. They arranged a meeting, during which they did little more than seek to persuade me that God had convinced them that I was the man they were to call as pastor.

I must say, I was flattered by all this attention! Just a few months ago no one had any interest in me as a pastor. Now numerous churches sought me — even the First Baptist Church of Collegetown, and even though I pointed out to them all the reasons why I was not the man for them. And I gave them plenty of reasons! I was short on experience; I had not finished my college or seminary work; I was unmarried; on and on I went. But this didn't seem to matter to them at all. They remained persistent with the plea that they were following God's will after much prayer. They said they had tried to leave me out of their plans, and had even heard others preach, and had talked seriously with several men, only to be drawn back each time to me.

I asked them to give me several weeks to pray about the matter before I agreed to meet with them. Then word came that I knew would settle the matter: I learned that Dr Bloom, the man who had promised he would warn everyone against me and my doctrinal tendencies, was a member of that church. When I heard this, I heaved a sigh of relief, thinking that the issue of First Baptist Church of Collegetown was now settled.

15.
Can man seek God?

As the afterglow of the revival continued, and as I put off representatives of various other churches, hoping time would settle the issue and discourage their pursuit, I began discussing theology with Terry on our regular Friday evening dates. We both thrived on the format — not that all we did was discuss theology! We had our share of special moments, but I must admit, it kept the relationship from moving in a direction in which many couples are tempted to go during courtship!

The first area of our concern was the doctrine of total depravity. We had decided to take the five points of the acrostic one at a time, and do several things. First, I would share with Terry my notes defining the subject which I had gathered in my discussions with Dr Sisk. Second, we would ask if the Calvinist conviction was scriptural — could we prove the doctrine, or disprove it from Scripture? Third, if Scripture disproved it, we would move on to the next point, but if Scripture proved the doctrine to be correct, we would then deal with the objections I had raised earlier, or which we might still raise even now.

So, after I had explained the doctrine of total depravity to Terry, we asked the question, 'Is it scriptural?' Does the Bible teach that man is powerless in the spiritual realm, and that he neither desires God, nor would seek God, unless God first sought and enabled him? Is man's will fallen and enslaved, along with his mind and emotions and desires?

To our surprise, we began to turn up numerous passages which seemed to confirm this. One of these was Romans 3:10-12, which was emphatic in declaring several things:

1. No one is righteous in his person or works.
2. No one seeks God.
3. No one understands God or spiritual matters.
4. All have gone astray and become unprofitable.
5. No one does any good.

But we also found verses which stated man had a responsibility to seek God: 'Seek the Lord while He may be found, call upon Him while He is near' (Isaiah 55:6). 'Seek first the kingdom of God and His righteousness, and all these things shall be added to you' (Matthew 6:33). 'Unless you repent you will all likewise perish' (Luke 13:3).

As we weighed these passages against one another, we concluded the following possibilities: either the Bible contained a contradiction; or one set of these verses is wrong and the other is right; or, thirdly, man is able to overcome his inability and do something by his own power which God says he cannot do by his fallen nature; or else man is able to meet the responsibility that God's commands require of him by God's power as God enables him.

The first two possibilities were ruled out by our view of a trustworthy and inspired Scripture. The third was ruled out as a contradiction in terms — that is, man cannot do by his own power something which is absolutely foreign to his own nature. Our conclusion was that the last of the four alternatives had to be correct. God does place upon man the responsibility to repent of sin and believe in Christ, but man is powerless to do so in his own strength, and he can only do so as the power of God enables him.

It was at this point that the 'whosoever will' passages of the Bible became clear. True, the Bible invites, 'Whoever desires, let him take of the water of life freely' (Revelation 22:17). It also speaks of Christ's death so that 'Whoever believes in Him should not perish but have everlasting life,' in John 3:16. But in the light of our conclusions from Romans 3, we concluded man could not come to God in his own strength, but his will had to be enabled by God!

Our conclusions in this area were further confirmed when we considered Ephesians 2:1-3. That passage indicated that before salvation (the quickening by God):

1. Man is *dead* in trespasses and sins;
2. Man walks according to the course of this world;

3. Man walks according to the dictates of Satan;
4. Man walks in the lust of his flesh, fulfilling the desires of the flesh and of the world.
5. Man is *by nature* a child of wrath.

We concluded this did not leave man any room for spiritual ability. How much spiritual ability could a dead man have in his mind, or his will, or his desires? If man already had all this spiritual ability (as some claimed), why was there a need for God to make him alive? Was not the quickening, or new birth, for the purpose of raising man from a state of powerless inability—a state from which he could not extricate himself by his own power?

Thus, it was clear that at the Fall man became totally incapable and powerless either to desire God, to serve God, to know God or to seek him unless God enabled him.

There was one other question which we did not consider that evening—we thought of it but didn't have time to pursue it. Does God just give new life to some, that they should be saved—those he has chosen by his will while bypassing others? Or does he remove the effects of the Fall at some point from all men, bringing each man and woman to a neutralized position where the individual can then either choose or reject Christ and salvation? Does God lift each individual up, as a father might lift his child up to the branch of an apple tree, so he could then decide to pick or not to pick an apple? We decided that question would best be asked after considering the second point of the Calvinist acrostic.

As I drove back to the hall of residence that night, I thought, 'What a way to spend a date! Old Todd would never believe it!'

It was late when I arrived back at the hall. I thought everyone (including Todd) would be in bed. Instead, he was awake, a light was on in the corner, and it was clear he had been crying. When I spoke to him, all I heard in return was a muffled response, followed quickly thereafter by an outburst of open sobbing. When I sought to ask him in a compassionate manner what in the world was wrong, he replied that it wouldn't do any good to tell me—no one could help him at this point in his life. I felt a little ashamed as I insisted I would like to help him if at all possible, while admitting in my heart only to myself, that I hoped it wasn't another of his schemes to get some money out of me.

Finally, he told me he was in deep trouble, as the young lady he had been going out with was pregnant. I was stunned. I knew old Todd had his weaknesses, and that he liked to talk a lot about his mannish ways, but I never thought it could come to this. I got out my Bible, read Scripture to him and sought to show him the enormity of his sin and the need to break with it and to find forgiveness and cleansing in the blood of Christ.

After we had prayed together, in which he poured his heart out to God in a serious manner such as I had never seen in him before, he seemed much better. But the sober understanding that he still faced some serious questions about the girl and his future cast a pall over our room, not only for that night, but for the next few days to come.

16.
The basis of God's choice

Revival continued the following Sunday at the church! The crowds were so large at both services that we had to bring in extra chairs, and some of the children sat on the floor, as we had done during the special week of meetings. People continued to profess faith in Christ. When one looked at the church and the rural community, one could only wonder where all those people came from. And, as on each Sunday after the misson services closed, representatives from several other churches were present.

On the Monday, I clashed once again with Dr Bloom. As I was passing his office on the way to a class, he beckoned to me to come in for a minute. I had no idea what to expect from him, but I knew it must be serious because for the first time that I had ever been in his office, he didn't make me sit down and wait!

Boldly, he plunged straight into his attack, saying, 'Young man, I don't know what you've said, or done, or are doing, to capture the attention of our pulpit committee, but I want you to stop!'

I tried to speak up to assure him I had done, and was doing, nothing, but he continued: 'Whatever it is — stop it, or I will put a stop to it, even if I have to take the matter to the highest ranks of this college and of the denomination!'

With that he abruptly dismissed me, not even allowing me to speak one word of explanation! I left his office thinking, 'Now I am accused falsely of two matters by the same man — first, of being a Calvinist, and second, of scheming to get a church, when in reality, I have been doing all I can to fight them off. And the man wouldn't even let me explain!'

Though Dr Bloom's ultimatum (which was out of my hands anyway) troubled me through the week, still it did not stop the days from rolling quickly by. I was glad to see Terry on Friday night, and I filled her in on the events of the past week (Todd and Dr Bloom) as we ate a bit of supper at one of the local restaurants. Her reaction to both events was the same as mine — she was heartbroken over Todd and appalled at Dr Bloom. She was a comfort and encouragement to me as we shared the matter together.

When we arrived back at her home, we got everything ready for a few hours of theological study. After going over from my notes the Calvinist position of unconditional election, we set out on our previously decided plan to ask the question: 'Is the doctrine scriptural?' As we pored over numerous Bible verses, we had to conclude that there is a biblical doctrine of election. Too many verses spoke about 'election', 'the elect', 'chosen' and similar expressions, for us to be able to deny that the Bible does teach election. Such a passage as Ephesians 1 spoke of God choosing a people from the foundation of the world.

The question, we decided, was not, 'Has God chosen or elected a people to be his own?' Rather the question was, '*On what basis* did God choose this people to be his own?' In seeking to answer this question, we noted two possibilities: either because of something God foresaw in man — whether in the way of goodness, or in relation to a coming faith, that is, that a person was going to believe; or because of the will of God, and the will of God alone, which also meant that God did not choose a man because of any foreseen faith or goodness.

Next, we sought to write down the arguments for each position. We noted that those who held to election based on foreseen faith (prescience) did so on the ground of passages which said we were elect according to the foreknowledge of God (Romans 8:29; 1 Peter 1:1-2). Those who held to election on the basis of God's sovereign will did so on the ground of Ephesians 1:5-6,11.

Our next step was to test each of these positions. We decided we had to ask the following questions:

1. What was the Greek word for 'foreknowledge', and what was its meaning?
2. Could Ephesians 1:5-6, 11 be interpreted in any other consistent manner than to mean election by divine sovereign grace?

3. How did both of these positions square with our previous conclusions concerning total depravity?

I found, as I looked at some Greek lexicons I had brought with me in my briefcase (Terry calls it a suitcase), that the Greek words in Romans 8:29 and 1 Peter 1:1-2 could carry the meaning of prescience or the sense of foreordination. That really didn't help us at all! How much easier it would have been if the words involved had only had one meaning! The question now was, 'Where do we go from here?'

'Perhaps,' I suggested to Terry, 'the context or grammar of the passage will help.'

Romans 8:29. We decided to concentrate on Romans 8:29. We took the passage apart grammatically, noticing that in verses 29-30 God was acting (or had acted), doing several things: he foreknew; he predestined; he called; he justified; he glorified.

We next asked, what was the object of the verb in each instance? On the one hand, was it faith, or something in a person? Or on the other hand, was it a person? We had to conclude that the object of each of these verbs was 'whom' — evidently a person and not the person's faith or anything in him or her: '*Whom* [God] foreknew, He also predestined... *whom* He predestined, these He also called... *whom* He called, He also justified and *whom* He justified, these He also glorified.'

The context was also helpful. It was a section of encouragement to God's people. Paul was speaking to the believer waiting patiently for the final consummation of all things, along with the whole creation. As he waits the Spirit of God assists him (vv. 26-27). Also as he waits he is assured of each event he encounters being from God's hand (v. 28). Then follows the reference to foreknowledge as it adds to the hope of the believer. Paul's point seems to be that the future hope of the believer is that God is in control of all things, including salvation. God foreknew; God predestinated; God called; God justified; God glorified. On that basis, no one can be against the elect (v. 31). He will freely give the elect all things! (v. 32). No one shall lay anything to their charge (v. 33); no one can condemn them (v. 34); and, finally, nothing shall separate them from the love of Christ (vv. 35-39). The whole context is God! God! God! And because of what God has done, the believer's present standing and future are certain.

On the other hand, to interpret Romans 8:29 as God foreseeing faith in someone (and really the grammatical construction leaves us no room for such a possibility) would be to substitute man in one part of the equation instead of God. This, we determined, would be incorrect.

Finally, we could find no other Scripture that even hinted that God chose the elect on the basis of any foreknowledge of their faith. Romans 8:29 indicated that God foreknew *individuals,* and not faith, and with this the remainder of Scripture agreed. Therefore the fact that in Romans 8:29 foreknowledge meant foreordination, instead of prescience, became a guide for interpreting 1 Peter 1:1-2 in the same manner.

Ephesians 1:5-6, 11. The Ephesians 1 passage was also clear. We noted the following truths:

    1. God has a people he has chosen (v. 4)
    2. God chose this people before the foundation of the world (v. 4)
    3. God's choice and predestination were on the basis of the good pleasure of his will (v. 5)
    4. All was done to the praise of the glory of his grace (v. 6)

On the fourth point we acknowledged that election on the basis of man's foreseen faith would glorify man rather than God, while election based on God's sovereign grace alone would truly bring praise to the glory of his grace.

Concerning the question of squaring this view of election with our previous conclusions about total depravity, we found full agreement between the two doctrines. According to the doctrine of total depravity (man's total inability to desire or seek God unless God enables him to do so) election based on foreknowledge defined as prescience was ruled out. Such a depraved being could not, and would not, choose God; therefore election could not be on this basis. It had to be on the basis of God's sovereign grace.

Thus we concluded that we not only believed in total depravity, but also in unconditional election, that is, an election not based on any condition in man, but completely on the will of God. One question in this area remained: how could this be, and God still be just? We decided to deal with it first thing next week.

I arrived back at college rather late again. Todd was still out. Just as I was crawling into bed, he came through the door with his old cheshire-cat smile (really a mischievous grin) on his face. It had been a week or so since I had seen that look on him. I knew he was back to his old self when he remarked flippantly, 'Guess what?'

'What?' I asked, more interested than usual since he hadn't been in such a mood for a while.

'It was a false alarm!' he declared.

'What was a false alarm?' I wanted to know.

'The girl being in a family way was a false alarm!'

'So how does that change anything?' I wondered aloud.

'Well,' he said with a wink, 'just erase from your mind and the record everything this past week! It was all unnecessary and now forgotten!'

'Unnecessary and forgotten?' I exclaimed, horrified. 'You mean you're covering your sin with the thin veneer and false coating of "I did it but it didn't really catch up with me, so now I can forget it"? What about all that sorrow and so-called repentance? What about those tears of supposed remorse? It appears to me you had little conviction or concern for your sin, but only that you got caught.'

His answer took me even more by surprise, as he started to blame the girl for the whole thing. 'Come on,' he said, 'Don't be so straitlaced. I've learned my lesson. I'll never let a girl get me in that kind of a mess again, believe me. I think she led me into the whole thing so I would marry her.'

With that I turned over in bed, closed my eyes and thought on the matter till I drifted off to sleep. I concluded I had just learned the difference between true and false repentance, and that false repentance can certainly resemble the real thing. I even began to wonder if Todd was really a Christian all, in the light of his careless attitude and his flippant lifestyle.

17.
A pressing invitation

On Saturday morning, following the consideration of doctrine with Terry and the scene with Todd, a phone-call came as I was getting ready to leave for my church visitation work. It was from the pulpit committee chairman of the First Baptist Church. He insisted that I have breakfast with him. I agreed since I had planned to stop somewhere for breakfast anyway.

As we met at a local restaurant, he reiterated the conviction of their committee that I was the man for their church. I raised again all my objections — my age, my lack of a college degree, my need for a seminary education, my single state, etc. He refused to consider any of them as prohibitive.

So, I finally pulled out my ultimate argument — Dr Bloom. I told him, 'You've got one man in your church who will oppose my coming, even if he has to take it to the college officials or the highest ranks of the denomination.'

He was obviously shocked and imediately asked, 'Who has been in touch with you to make such a threat?'

'Dr Bloom!' I replied. 'He has accused me not only of pursuing the church, but also of being a Calvinist.'

He got quite upset at this point: 'He's way out of line! I don't know about the accusation of being a Calvinist, but I *know* you haven't pursued this church — we've pursued you, and you barely will give us the time of day!'

Then he made a proposition: 'Look, why don't you come and preach for us one weekend? It won't be a trial sermon, but just an opportunity for you to see our church, and for our church to see you.

On that Sunday afternoon you can meet with the pulpit committee to do one of several things: either ask us questions about the church, if God has created an interest in the work; or you can tell us to get lost and never bother you again; or ask us to pray about the matter further, while you continue to seek God's will on the issue. And you let us take care of Dr Bloom!'

His last remark was the most interesting of all at the time. Maybe, I thought, they could give me some relief from Dr Bloom. Maybe they could tell him the facts of the case, rather than my having to try to defend myself. Also, it might give me an opportunity to convince them once and for all I was not their man and put an end to their pursuit of me.

So, I agreed to his suggestion, and we set a date about a month off so I could make arrangements at my own church. I was really interested to see how they would deal with Dr Bloom! That alone would make the weekend worthwhile.

During the rest of the week, following a busy Sunday, I gave much thought to the question Terry and I were to discuss the next Friday — how the view of unconditional election could leave us with a just God. Several lines of thought began to develop in my mind.

First, I wondered whose definition of justice one could use to test God's actions! If he is God, should he not be the one to define and determine what constituted justice and just actions?

Second, when did God's decree of election take place in relation to man's fall? Could it be that, if the decree relating to the Fall came first, and was followed by the decree to elect some, then the accusation of injustice against unconditional election would have no ground? I set aside a free afternoon to do some further reading in this area before meeting with Terry.

The rest of the weekend was fairly normal except for an encounter with Jim Mitchell, the former pastor at Lime Creek. I ran into him in a local shop, and he was still complaining about my getting credit for the work he started. Then he had the nerve to ask me if I would recommend him to a certain church which was without a pastor. His argument was that since he was the one who had laid the groundwork for the working of God at Lime Creek, then I should have no question in recommending him to another church, even though his Lime Creek pastorate had been controversial.

Then I made the mistake of raising the wrong question! I asked him if he was still an unbalanced Calvinist who would do again the same things he did at Lime Creek — use of unknown terminology to the people; theological lectures instead of biblical sermons; long, unending sermons; an air of superiority; each sermon a theological dissertation on one of the five points of Calvinism; and the use of 'thee' and 'thou' in his sermons.

My question was meant to help me determine if I could, or could not, recommend him, but he didn't take it that way. He apparently saw it as an accusation of incompetence for the ministry, and instead of answering me, he whirled round and walked out of the shop without saying another word. Obviously, he felt I had no right to question him, his beliefs or practices, and regarded me as a theological novice who was incapable, or unworthy, of any discussions with such a brilliant mind as his!

I did come to a conclusion that I hoped I would remember. I was convinced that his extreme form of Calvinism was not his main problem! His main problem was one of personality. I also noted that the ministry often drew strange personalities. I was not questioning any man's call to preach, but I saw that the ministry could well be of interest to a man if he wanted, or liked, to be the centre of attention, or if he wanted some authority over others, or thrived on the thrill of importance. Couple that personality weakness with an unbalanced view of any theology, including Calvinism, and it could create a monster capable of an incalculable amount of damage to a church and the souls in it.

At the same time I realized that not every church problem is necessarily a personality problem on the part of the pastor. Personality problems can exist in the other members of the church and can create equal havoc. Couple the strange twists of personalities with certain twists of theology, and add to that a membership in some churches of those who have never been born again, and the problems are compounded.

But then again, I had to admit that not all church problems are personality problems. True, the personality can get in the way and create chaos, but problems can also legitimately come over truth and doctrine, even when personalities are under control.

Some people would attribute all church problems to questions of personality. Others would say they are mostly doctrinal. I concluded the basis could be either, but whatever the principal cause, at least one other element would no doubt also be involved somewhere along the line. A problem in personality could make a legitimate doctrinal problem even greater, and vice-versa.

I was amazed at what the Lord was teaching me!

18.
Is it fair?

On the next Friday evening Terry and I tackled the questions left over from the previous week — did unconditional election leave us with an unjust God? That is to say, if God chose the elect on the basis of his sovereign will alone, and without consideration of anything in man, then would not God be unjust in choosing one and bypassing another? We reached several conclusions.

First, if God's decree of election *followed* the decree of the fall of man (this view, I learned, was called infralapsarianism), then all men were seen at the decree of election as undeserving of God's grace. Not only that, all were deserving of eternal hell and certainly had no basis to claim God's grace or love. Therefore, how could anyone accuse God of being unjust if he chose on the basis of his sovereign will to save a people from this fallen and undeserving mass?

Secondly, even if we refused to consider the order of the decrees, or if we were to place the decree to elect before the decree to allow the Fall (this view is called supralapsarianism), that would not make God unfair or unjust either. We reached this conclusion by consulting an English dictionary to define these words that men so often say would apply to God, if unconditional election were true. We noted the following words and definitions:

> *Arbitrary:* based on, or subject to, one's opinion, judgement, prejudice, etc.; absolute, despotic.
> *Despot:* an absolute monarch; an autocrat; a tyrant.
> *Despotism:* unlimited authority; absolute power.

Tyrant: one who rules oppressively or cruelly; a despot; one who exercises absolute power without legal warrant, whether ruling well or badly.

Autocrat: a supreme ruler of unrestricted power; an arrogant, dictatorial person.

Dictator: a person having absolute power of government; especially one considered to be an oppressor; one who rules, prescribes or subjugates authoritatively.

Next, we noted reasons why these words could not be used in reference to God even if unconditional election was true.

1. All of the above words are used to speak of equals in relating to one another. But God and man are not equals! God is God, the eternal sovereign, and man is man, the limited creature. To use these words of God is to press upon God an equality with man, and to judge God by human standards and definitions of justice.

2. All of the above words, if applied to election and reprobation, ignore completely the fall of man and man's condemnation, and the fact that man deserves nothing before God, except wrath and judgement.

Our conclusion was that unconditional election was not only biblical, but was also defensible before the accusations usually raised against it. We spent the rest of the evening in awe as we contemplated God's electing grace, which had been manifested to us. We concluded that we could ask many questions about grace (What is it? What are its results, etc.?), but why grace is manifested is not one of them. The mere nature and definition of grace will not permit any such questions as to why God showers grace upon any, that is, upon even a single fallen and undeserving sinner.

We also agreed that evening that our doctrinal study would have to be delayed until after the end of term and after the weekend preaching engagement at First Baptist Church in Collegetown. Besides, we felt a need to do some more reading and studying before tackling the doctrine of limited atonement.

19.
A difficult meeting

The weekend at First Baptist Church of Collegetown was uneventful until the Sunday afternoon meeting with the pulpit committee, which somehow, to my surprise, became an open church meeting with a certain person very much in evidence! I nearly didn't stay for the meeting, since I had been told it would be the pulpit committee only, and since my old nemesis, Dr Bloom, was present for who knew what purpose? Also, I wondered how they were going to conduct such a meeting, when I had been told by the chairman of the pulpit committee that this would be *my* chance to tell them either to get lost, to pray further about the matter, or to ask questions about the church. I also wondered what had happened to the chairman's promise to take care of the problem with Dr Bloom. (I found out later that it was Dr Bloom who had insisted on such a set-up!)

He was present at all three of the weekend services (which had been feebly attended), and he sat with a non-committal look, and spoke not a single word to me about anything, let alone one of the sermons. At the end of each service he vanished, almost as if magically leaving by some supernatural power at some uncommon exit. To say I felt overwhelmingly uneasy over this surprise Sunday afternoon setting would be fully accurate and correct. I decided to listen and find out what direction the meeting would take before uttering a word.

The chairman of the pulpit committee began the service by leading in prayer (a general prayer from which I learned nothing of what to expect in the procedures to follow). Next, he gave an accurate explanation of the purpose of the meeting, and apologized to me for expanding the meeting from the pulpit committee to the open congregation. Finally, he asked me if I had anything to say.

Having learned in my own church business meetings that so often the best defence is a good attack, I put the issue back in his court by suggesting he explain clearly to all that I had not sought, and was not seeking the church, but had agreed to come at the insistence of the pulpit committee, based on their convictions concerning my ministry and their present situation as a church without a pastor. This he did, and the ball was back in my court.

So I spoke out, thanking them for the enjoyable weekend, for their hospitality and encouragement, and for the honour they had bestowed upon me by even thinking I might be a candidate for their pulpit. Yet, I told them I had to be honest with them — I still had too many questions in my mind to allow the issue to go any further. I wasn't sure the Lord was finished with me at Lime Creek. I wasn't sure I could handle the larger pastorate (a large church and membership, even though the attendance was very small). I wasn't sure about my future education. I was sure about my marriage, but we hadn't yet fixed a date for the wedding, which meant I would be their pastor for some months, or maybe even a couple of years, as a single man, which might not be best for the church. I also gave several other reasons why I was sure that their enthusiasm and conviction concerning me were misplaced.

When I had finished (and my speech included a request to let me pray about it further) the chairman asked if anyone in the congregation wanted to speak. It gave a big boost to my ego as numerous people (unknown to me and unsolicited by me) rose to say what a marvellous blessing the three messages had been to them, and how they, along with the pulpit committee, were convinced I was the man for their church in spite of all my objections.

It was at this point that Dr Bloom rose to speak. I braced myself spiritually and emotionally as he began. He gave a history of the church (evidently he had been one of the very early members as a young professor just out of seminary), and then he spoke his conviction. He felt it would be a mistake to call this young preacher-boy (a term he used derogatorily) to be the pastor, not only because of all the reasons given, but also because he was unsound in the faith.

'Do you know,' he bellowed, 'that this man is a Calvinist, and Calvinists have a distorted view of God which ruins evangelism and missions? Besides that, I have given the pulpit committee the names of numerous older and more stable and doctrinally sound men — men they have refused to consider. I don't know how this young man has so mesmerized you all! Believe me, he is not for our church. I know him, as I have had him as a student, and I have clashed with him before over doctrine as I sought to help him understand Baptist doctrine for our day. He is narrow, bigoted, unteachable and rebellious against authority, as well as non-Baptistic in doctrine. I do hope you all, including the pulpit committee, give up your pursuit of him and realize he may be pursuing this church by reverse psychology as he is playing hard to get. Please look for a pastor from one of the countless good men who are faithful to our denomination and doctrine!'

As he sat down, I thought, 'Well, Mr Chairman, you really did take care of Dr Bloom! You let him make every false accusation against me in the book!'

I also wondered how I could ever begin to reply or defend myself against all those accusations — a distorted view of God; a killer of missions and evangelism; narrow, bigoted, unteachable and rebellious; non-Baptistic in doctrine; pursuing the church; and who knows what else? And all because he perceived me to be a Calvinist — which I was not!

Only when it was obvious the chairman of the pulpit committee was not going to come to my aid, did I reply. Rather than defend myself point by point, I said with a smile, 'If I were all those things Dr Bloom accuses me of being, I wonder how I ever was ordained; or how Lime Creek Baptist Church ever called me; or how we ever saw such a great revival and salvation of souls in the church this spring; or how I ever am allowed to stay in college! My life and record of ministry are open to anyone who wishes to examine them, rather than listen to the false accusations of another. I assure you, if I ever become a candidate to pastor your church, you can ask me about any or all of these accusations. But now, I am your guest, and the discussion of these issues, I feel, is not only unnecessary at this point, but out of order. Yet even in God's providence, he may have used Dr Bloom to close the door to any possibility for me to pastor here, which is fine with me, if that be God's will. I will take it all as an answer to my prayer for direction. So, Mr Chairman, I suggest we close this meeting with prayer and busy ourselves to get ready for the evening service.'

In view of the fact that there was a heavy spirit in the air, he followed my suggestion. The evening service was difficult for me. I left the church and drove to Terry's house after the service, sighing inwardly, 'I'm glad that's over!' and with a certainty that the afternoon meeting had ended First Baptist Church's interest in me and mine in them. I could hardly wait till next Sunday to see my own people and to get back into the pulpit at Lime Creek! Anyway, who wanted to be pastor to fifty people in a building that seated a thousand?

20.
For whom did Christ die?

The conviction that Lime Creek Baptist Church was God's will for my life was strong, at least for the first few days after my experience at First Baptist Church. But as time went by my heart began to sense a deep burden for those people. I couldn't get the picture of fifty people in that vast building out of my mind! What a pitiful scene! And then there were the testimonies about how much the preaching of the Word of God had meant to them! It was the picture of people dying in a desert place. I began to wrestle with the question of how a person could know God's will for his life.

The next Friday evening Terry and I began our approach to the doctrine of limited, or particular, atonement. As usual, I reviewed the doctrine for Terry's sake. We saw that:

1. Limited atonement states that the death of Christ had a particular design and purpose towards the elect, rather than just a general design and purpose towards all men.

2. Limited atonement states that because God's particular design in the atonement is for the elect, and so the salvation of the elect is guaranteed. Any other purpose or design in election would only make *possible* the salvation of all men but would *guarantee* the salvation of no man.

3 Limited atonement is the logical result of the first two points of Calvinism. If man is totally depraved and he cannot, and does not, come to God except on the basis of election, then atonement must be made for the elect, or they would not be able to be saved.

4. Limited atonement says, on the other hand, if there is such a thing as election, and some are not of the elect, then there would be no reason nor necessity for Christ to die for the non-elect. If Christ had died for all men in the same manner, that means he died and made atonement for those who were not elect, which would mean there would be those in hell for whom Christ had died and for whom he had made an atonement for sin.

Having reviewed the doctrine, our next step was to test whether the doctrine was scriptural. In tracing and recalling verses about Christ's death, we wrote down the following verses which spoke of Christ's death for his people.

'I am the good shepherd; the good shepherd gives His life *for the sheep*'(John 10:11).
'Christ ... loved *the church* and *gave Himself for it*, that He might sanctify and cleanse it with the washing of water by the word, that He might present it to Himself a glorious church, not having spot or wrinkle, or any such thing, but that it should be holy and without blemish' (Ephesians 5:25-27).
'Therefore take heed to yourselves and to all the flock, among which the Holy Spirit has made you overseers, to shepherd *the church of God, which He purchased with His own blood*' (Acts 20:28).
'Therefore, in all things He had to be made like His brethren, that He might be a merciful and faithful High Priest in things pertaining to God, *to make propitiation for the sins of the people*' (Hebrews 2:17).

We also listed several other verses which taught the same thing, such as the following: Matthew 20:28; Mark 10:45; 14:23-24; Luke 1: 68-69; Titus 2:14; Hebrews 9:12-15, 28; 10:14; 1 Peter 1:19-21; 2:24; Revelation 1:5-6.
Over against this set of verses, we noted other passages which indicated a general nature of the atonement:

'And many more believed because of His own word. Then they said to the woman, "Now we believe, not because of what you said, for we have heard for ourselves and know that this is indeed the Christ, *the Saviour of the world*'" (John 4:41-42).

'For to this end we both labour and suffer reproach, because we trust in the living God, who is *the Saviour of all men,* especially of those who believe' (1 Timothy 4:10).

'And we have seen and testify that the Father has sent the Son as *Saviour of the world*' (1 John 4:14).

'For God so loved *the world* that He gave His only begotten Son, that whoever believes in Him should not perish, but have everlasting life' (John 3:16).

'The next day John saw Jesus coming toward him, and said, "Behold! The Lamb of God *who takes away the sin of the world!*"' (John 1:29).

'That is, that God was in Christ *reconciling the world to Himself,* not imputing their trespasses to them' (2 Corinthians 5:19).

'For this is good and acceptable in the sight of God our Saviour, who desires *all men to be saved* and to come to the knowledge of the truth. For there is one God, and one Mediator between God and men, the Man Christ Jesus, *who gave Himself a ransom for all,* to be testified in due time' (1 Timothy 2:3-6).

'But we see Jesus, who was made a little lower than the angels, for the suffering of death crowned with glory and honour, that He, by the grace of God, *might taste death for everyone*' (Hebrews 2:9).

'And He Himself is the propitiation for our sins, and not for ours only, but also for *the whole world*' (1 John 2:2).

As we read and reread these verses, the following possibilities, thoughts and conclusions emerged to solve the seeming contradiction.

1. The first possibility we considered was that *there is a contradiction* in the Bible, for it states that Christ died for the church (the elect), and also for every lost person in the world. We ruled out this possibility because of our presuppositions concerning the nature of Scripture. There are no contradictions in the Word of God. Therefore, somehow these two sets of statements must and can be reconciled.

2. The second possibility we looked at was that *the Bible teaches a universalism,* i. e., that all men will be saved. If Christ

is the Saviour of the world (meaning all men and women of the world), then the whole world will be saved. If he is the Saviour of all men, then all men will be saved. If he takes away the sin of the world (meaning all men and women of the world), then the whole of humanity will be saved. If he reconciled the world (meaning all men and women of the world) to himself, then all men and women will be saved. If he gave himself as a ransom for every individual, then every individual will be saved. If he tasted death for every single person, then every single person will be saved. If he is the propitiation for the sins of the world (meaning all men and women of the world), then all men and women will be saved.

We ruled out this possibility in the light of the clear teaching of other passages of Scripture, such as the following:

John 3:16 implies that the one who does not believe in Christ will perish.

'He who does not believe is condemned already, because he has not believed in the name of the only begotten Son of God' (John 3:18).

'He who believes in the Son has everlasting life; and he who does not believe the Son shall not see life, but the wrath of God abides on him' (John 3:36).

In John 5:24 the one who does not believe in Christ will come into judgement.

'And do not fear those who kill the body but cannot kill the soul. But rather fear Him who is able to destroy both soul and body in hell' (Matthew 10:28).

3. The third possibility we considered was that Christ died for the elect in that *he made a general atonement* for the sins of all men and women, which included the sins of the elect as well.

This would mean that Christ died for the elect in the same way that he died for those who were not elect, and his death for the non-elect was the same as his death for the elect. The answer to the question, 'How does this view differ from universalism?' is that, on this view, men and women must accept this atonement, and those who do not will not be saved — the wrath of God abides and will abide on them for eternity.

We had to admit that this view looked plausible and very inviting! But in view of the time (it was well past midnight), we decided to stop our search at this point for the time being. We agreed to think about this suggestion and to take up our discussion next Friday night with this third possibility.

As I drove back to college, I was startled by flashing red and blue lights as I came around one of the 'dangerous' bends in the road. I noticed a body on a stretcher being placed in the ambulance, and it looked like Todd climbing in behind. I couldn't see the car because it was off the road, and if it was Todd, it was probably a borrowed one anyway.

As the ambulance sped away towards the hospital, I followed in pursuit, though trying not to break the speed limit. Obviously, I arrived at the hospital well after the ambulance, but did find Todd in the emergency room crying again, almost as sorrowfully as he had on the night he thought he was in trouble.

He was glad to see me, and grabbed hold of me and held on tightly as he wept. When I asked what had happened, he replied that he had been on a date and they had had a crash and the girl was dead!

21.
Towards an answer

The first few days of the next week were spent with Todd, helping him through the ordeal of the young lady's death. There was not only the funeral, but many hours were spent just talking in our room, both before and after the services. In our discussion, which was guided by Scripture and many of the truths that God was teaching me, it became clear to both myself and Todd that he was not truly saved.

Finally on Thursday evening the burden was so heavy that he dashed from our room, once again weeping uncontrollably. I decided not to try to follow him, but to leave him in the Lord's hands. Two hours later he returned, with a different countenance and manner. He declared that God had saved him as he walked and thought on his life and his sin. He came to see in those two hours the grace of God to sinners and, as he walked, that grace had touched and saved him. We wept together as we hugged one another, rejoicing.

Then he said, 'Ira, I want you to teach me everything you've been learning! Both these times you counselled me, you knew so much Scripture and so much truth! And your words and application of Scripture were so powerful! Ira, I want to be a man of the Word who can also preach and teach the Word like you! I'm tired of living a false, superficial life and preaching false, superficial sermons. Will you help me become a man of God and a preacher of the Word?' Without hesitation, I agreed to help!

When Friday evening arrived, I realized the events of the week hadn't allowed much time for deep reflection on the third possibility concerning the atonement which we had left unresolved the previous week. I pulled out our notes and we read together again the third possibility, which was that Christ died for the elect in that he made a general atonement for the sins of all men, which included the sins of the elect as well. We reminded ourselves that this meant that Christ died for the elect in the same way that he died for those who were not elect, and his death for the non-elect was the same as his death for the elect. We saw again that this view differed from universalism in that men must accept this atonement, and those who do not will not be saved — the wrath of God abides and will abide on them for eternity.

As we mulled over the problem, I said to Terry, 'There is another possibility, you know!'

'What is that ?' she wanted to know.

'Well, why don't you put the kettle on and get us something to eat while I write down some thoughts?'

Quickly I reviewed our past observations. The first possibility had been that *there is a contradiction in the Bible*, in the light of the two sets of Scripture, where one seemed to say that Christ died for the elect, and another seemed to say he died for all. We had ruled this possibility out on grounds of our commitment to an inerrant Scripture.

Secondly we had considered whether *the Bible teaches universalism*, that is, that all men and women will be saved since Christ died for all. We had ruled out this possibility in the light of the verses which clearly declare that the unbeliever will not be saved.

Finally, we had suggested that *the Bible teaches that Christ died for the elect and the non-elect in the same manner*. I had to admit I had problems with this third view as well! Had Christ died for the elect and the non-elect in the sense that he had made an atonement for the sins of both? But, did not atonement mean that he had satisfied all that the justice and law of God required of mankind as the condition of their being received into the favour of an eternal God? Does not the atonement mean that Christ was a substitute, assuming all the legal responsibility of those for whom he died? Thus, if he died for both the elect and the non-elect in the same manner, would not both be saved?

The issue here was not whether faith ever brought the application of that death or not, but in what sense did Christ die for each group? Was it an atoning death or not? If it was an atoning death, then the sins of all those for whom he died would be atoned for. Was it a satisfaction of the justice and law of God, or not? If it was, then all those for whom Christ had died would be acceptable to God. Was it a substitutionary death? Then all those for whom Christ died as a substitute would be received by God. Was it an assumption by Christ of legal responsibility? If so, then justice was satisfied for all those whose legal responsibility he had taken in his death.

Thus, if Christ had died for the elect and non-elect in the same manner, then it had been an atoning, substitutionary satisfaction of the legal responsibility, not only for the elect, but for the non-elect also. How could that be, in the light of the clear biblical teaching that the lost will be in hell? Will there really be those in hell for whom Christ has paid an atoning, substitutionary satisfaction?

On the other hand, if Christ's death for both was not a complete work (an atoning, substitutionary sacrifice for their legal responsibility), then how can even the elect be saved by a death which did not atone for sin, which was not a substitution and which did not fully satisfy the demands of God's law and justice concerning sin?

My conclusion had to be that Christ did not die for the elect and non-elect in the same way. His death for the elect was a complete work. He did indeed die as an atoning, substitutionary sacrifice which satisfied the demands of God's law and justice against sin. If we were to speak in any way at all of Christ having also died for the non-elect, it could not be in those terms.

This could also be the explanation for the two sets of passages concerning Christ's death for the elect and for all. Further study was needed to deal in depth with these verses, but I was overjoyed at my conclusions for the moment.

I explained my thinking concerning this possibility to Terry as we sipped coffee and munched cookies. We discussed the matter at length and she agreed with my conclusion that Christ's death for the elect and the non-elect could not have been the same.

But then she asked, 'How do you explain all these other verses?'

She had a good point. What does the Bible mean when it says that Christ is 'the Saviour of the world'? (John 4:41-42; 1 John 4:14). Or that Christ is 'the Saviour of *all men*'? (1 Timothy 4:10).

Or again what about the following passages?

'For God so loved *the world* that He gave His only begotten Son' (John 3:16).

'The Lamb of God, who takes away the sin of *the world*' (John 1:29).

'God was in Christ reconciling *the world* to Himself, not imputing their trespasses to them' (2 Corinthians 5:19).

'God our Saviour ... desires *all men* to be saved' (1 Timothy 2:3-4).

'Christ ... gave Himself a ransom for *all*' (1 Timothy 2:5-6).

'... that He, by the grace of God, might taste death for *everyone*' (Hebrews 2:9).

'Jesus Christ ... Himself is the propitiation for our sins, and not for ours only but also for the *whole world*' (1 John 2:2).

We agreed that these passages would form the basis of our discussion the next Friday night. As I drove back to college, I began to wonder when I would get time for study, especially now that summer school had started, and those sessions of study are even more hectic than the usual college terms.

However, I drifted off to sleep that night thinking, not about the limited atonement but about a question of limited attendance — the tiny congregation in that 1,000-seat building at First Baptist Church! The conviction was growing that perhaps the Lord wanted me there, after all, as pastor.

22.
A hospital visit

The best hours of the week for me (and I suppose for many pastors) are those after the Sunday evening service. I can then finally relax! It is the buffer zone between the escalating pressure of one week and the beginning of another. I usually spent that time over at Terry's just relaxing. We did not talk about church! We did not discuss theology! We did not meet with others! It was our time alone together to unwind and talk and to get better acquainted.

Such was the Sunday evening following our second discussion of the atonement, when the phone rang and Terry passed the call to me. My first thought was, 'Who in the church is in some need or trouble now?'

To my surprise it was not a member of my own congregation, but the chairman of the pulpit committee at First Baptist Church. He said, softly but firmly, 'I thought you'd like to know that we voted tonight to extend to you a call to come to be our pastor.'

I was shocked! They had voted to call me without my even hinting I was interested? How could they?

My silence must have told him of my shock, and he continued, offering further information as he spoke: 'I know we didn't have your permission, but the membership was insistent we do it ever since the Sunday you were with us. And the vote was unanimous!'

'Unanimous?' I asked, incredulous (in the light of Dr Bloom's presence).

'What about Dr Bloom?' I asked.

'That's another story,' he replied, with some conviction in his tone.

'Is it a story I need to know?' I asked.

'Well, you'll know all of it sooner or later, so I guess you just might as well know now. Dr Bloom suffered a heart attack this afternoon just a few hours before the evening service. He is in the hospital now. When it was announced in the morning service that a vote on you would be taken this evening, he made a scene and said such a vote would be passed only over his dead body! Well, it seems it almost came to that!'

I had not just mixed emotions as I hung up the phone, but scrambled emotions! First Baptist Church had called me as pastor unanimously and without my knowledge or permission! Dr Bloom was in hospital with a heart attack suffered just a few hours before the vote was to be taken, after making a scene over the church wanting to vote. And now I had a decision to make which was difficult in the light not only of my love and appreciation for the people of Lime Creek Baptist Church, but my burden for First Baptist Church and my strained relationship with a sick Dr Bloom.

I had asked the chairman of the pulpit committee for a week to pray about the matter. His reply was to take two weeks or even a month! They were convinced I was the man for their church, and they were willing to wait for God to burden my heart for the work. There was no more relaxing this Sunday evening — a burden was upon me!

The next day after my lectures, I made my way to the hospital in the hope of seeing Dr Bloom. Much debate of mind had gone before this decision. Many questions still remained even after I decided to go. Would he receive me? Was there a possibility my presence could make him worse? Would he make a scene and order me out of his room?

You might wonder why I had decided to go, if either of those things were likely to happen. I had checked and found his heart attack had not been as serious as originally supposed, since he was not in intensive care, but resting well in a private room. I had concluded that, regardless of the circumstances, or his action or attitude towards me, I had to act out of the motivation of love. That was my duty and obligation before the Lord. His reaction was his responsibility before the Lord.

Still it was with some anxiety that I made my way to his room and knocked on his door. I pushed the door open at the request of a muffled voice inside the room. As I did so, I also braced myself for whatever might follow. Not waiting for Dr Bloom to speak, I began immediately by saying, 'Dr Bloom, I just wondered how you were.'

His reply was as cold as his stare: 'Pointer, what are you doing here? You're not my pastor yet, and probably never will be, even though you might preach at First Baptist Church.' I noted he didn't say, 'be pastor at First Baptist Church'.

I tried to ignore his rudeness by asking if there was anything I could do for him. That obviously was the wrong thing to do as it opened the door for him to tell me I could get out and leave him alone.

I sought to remain cool and kind by asking, 'Can I pray for you before I go?'

His answer was a dig at my supposed theology, as he said, 'When a man is a Calvinist, like you are, Pointer, everything is predestined anyway. I don't see what stock you can put in prayer!'

With that he turned to face the window, which meant his back was towards me. I left, after saying graciously, 'I do hope you're back at college soon, sir.'

I went away with a heavy heart. I had so hoped the heart attack might have softened his attitude towards me. But such was evidently not the case. My mind turned back to summer school work, church work and the pressing decision concerning First Baptist Church. The question of limited or general atonement was on the back burner, at least for now, for I was a limited man in the number of hours in a day!

Yet Dr Bloom had made a statement which I pondered as I drove. What about prayer? Where does it fit in Calvinism? Does Calvinism make prayer unnecessary? I concluded that if Calvinism was scriptural, none the less the same Bible taught the necessity and need of prayer in doing the Lord's work, and therefore there would not be a contradiction between the two. Prayer must be part of the means that God uses to accomplish his purpose, and prayer must be part of the responsibility of man before God. Calvinism does not deny the responsibility of man — neither the unconverted man's responsibility to repent and believe, nor the believer's responsibility to live a godly life, including the means and privilege of prayer.

23.
A weekend conference

On the Saturday following, I attended a weekend conference which was advertised as centring on the doctrines of Calvinism. Several men were on the programme as scheduled to preach that day. I attended at the invitation of Jim Mitchell, the former pastor of Lime Creek. Though our last contact had been somewhat heated, he was friendly when he called and extended the invitation. He told me I had never attended, and never would attend anything like it, and he was right.

We arrived a few minutes before the morning service began, and found the church where the conference was being held comfortably full. We took our seats close to the front (the back seats were all taken), and I browsed through the programme, especially the speakers and subjects for the day. I saw that we were to hear six sermons, two in each of the scheduled services. The speakers were for the most part pastors, and the subjects were interesting, though some were rather theological.

Following twenty-five to thirty minutes of singing and announcements, the first speaker stepped onto the platform. His subject was the holiness of God, certainly a very sober subject, but to my surprise he spent fifteen minutes or so making people laugh. He spoke of various subjects and people he knew, but everything he said was designed to create humour and laughter. I thought such actions were hardly appropriate before any sermon, let alone a sermon on the holiness of God! I longed for him to read his text and get on with it.

But I should have known that a man who entertained before he preached would do no better when he finally came to the sermon. He did eventually read a text, but he did very little with it except generalize and wax emotional over it, stating some doctrine, but mostly attacking and lambasting everybody else, except Calvinists. He droned on for over an hour, which meant he preached for an hour and fifteen minutes, if you counted the 'joke time'. His sermon was more of a testimony to the unholiness of the preacher than the holiness of God!

I began to wonder if I was wasting my time at this conference when the second speaker of the morning preached on the Puritans instead of Scripture. After reading a text, he spent the rest of his time (an hour or so) reading quotations from the Puritans and then emphasizing what they had said. Like the first sermon, there was no real exposition of the text — no explanation of the context, no consideration of the grammar and syntax, no understanding of the words of the text and their meaning; and no clear outline to set forth the truth of the passage. And whereas the first man had entertained people to death, the second speaker bored his audience to death, and they never knew what he was trying to say overall. I began to wonder where these men had gained their ideas of what preaching was supposed to be.

As the former pastor and I went to lunch at one of the local restaurants, I was amazed to find that he had been enthralled by the two morning sermons. He admitted he didn't like the first speaker's 'joke time', but he liked what followed, and he had really devoured the quotes from the Puritans. I didn't want to be too cool or critical, but I told him that what I had heard that morning did not pass the test of biblical preaching. He didn't understand what I was saying, and the situation began to get heated, so not wanting another argument like the one we had the last time we were together, I shut up, and let him rave over the blessing of the morning. I, on the other hand, was praying the afternoon would not be the same. If it were, I wondered if I could stand the evening service.

To my joy, the afternoon session was not like the morning. We heard two fine and outstanding sermons. The content was there — the men had done their homework. Obviously, they were not out to get people, or shooting from the hip, as the first speaker of the morning appeared to do. Also, the content was well organized in an understandable framework, and delivered with compassion and humility, but with boldness and power. I was fed and challenged!

Even so, I decided to leave after the afternoon session. I needed to get ready for my own preaching responsibility the next day. Also, I was a little fearful of what the evening would hold. It seemed to me that I had heard the best and the worst the conference had to offer, and I had other responsibilities, so why hear any more — it could be more of the worst kind!

But I had learned something! To be a Calvinist does not guarantee a man knows how to preach or handle the Word of God. There is nothing about Calvinism that automatically produces capable preachers. In fact, a Calvinist preacher can make the same mistake, or mistakes, that other preachers make — weak handling of the text, shallow content, poor organization and an improper delivery. Perhaps a Calvinist might have a better theological foundation (assuming Calvinism is biblical), which would give him an advantage in the practice of the ministry, but I concluded that Calvinism is not the automatic cure-all for all the ills of the church.

24.
What does 'the world' mean?

The next Friday evening, Terry and I met to try to finalize our thoughts on the atonement. I hadn't tried to see Dr Bloom at the hospital again, but had prayed much about the matter, as well as the invitation to go to First Baptist Church as pastor. No decision had yet been made as to what I would do with either situation.

As Terry and I met that Friday night, we reviewed our thinking and conclusions that Christ had not died for the non-elect in the same manner as he had for the elect. His death was an atonement for the elect — that is, he had satisfied all that the justice and law of God required as the condition of their being received into the favour of an eternal God. The problem we now faced concerned the several verses of Scripture that seemed to indicate that his death was universally the same for elect and non-elect alike.

I drew Terry's attention to the fact that many of the problem passages contained the word 'world' and were found in the Gospel and epistles of John the apostle. I pointed out that John was a Jew and a key figure and leader in the Jerusalem church (Galatians 2:9), which was largely Jewish. I reminded her that Paul was an apostle to the Gentiles (Acts 9:15; 15:3, Romans 3:29; 11:11) and referred to the difficulties he encountered when he sought to convince his Jewish brothers in Christ that the church (the body of Christ) was made up of both Jews and Gentiles.

Paul fought this battle of the one-body concept of the church early in his ministry, as we can see from his epistle to the Galatians. He even carried the fight all the way to a council in Jerusalem (Acts 15), where the truth won, but still he had to battle for the application of the one-body principle in the lives of the churches. Paul was finally arrested for this concept (Ephesians 3:1 — the mystery he speaks of in this verse is that the church is composed of both Jews and Gentiles — see also 2 Timothy 1:1-2; Acts 21:28; 22:1-22).

With this background, we were ready to seek understanding of the 'world' passages written by John, particularly the following:

'This is ... the Christ, the Saviour of the *world*' (John 4:41-42).

'The Father has sent the Son as Saviour of the *world*'(1 John 4:14).

'For God so loved the *world* that He gave His only begotten Son' (John 3:16)

'Behold! The Lamb of God who takes away the sin of the *world*!' (John 1:29).

'He Himself is the propitiation for our sins, and not for ours only, but also for the *whole world*' (1John 2:2).

I suggested to Terry that what John is really saying in these passages is that Christ died for men *from all nations*, with a special reference to the Gentiles, and not just for the Jews alone.

I explained what I meant by looking at each of the phrases in turn:

'If he is literally Saviour of the world (of every man and woman in the world), then all will be saved. But surely John is saying rather that he is Saviour not only of Jews, but even of Gentiles?

'If Christ literally takes away the sin of the world (the sin of every person in the world), then everyone will be saved. But surely what John is saying is that he takes away the sin of both Jews and Gentiles, and not just Jews?

'If he is literally the propitiation for the sins of the world (every man and woman), then again, all will be saved. But isn't John really saying that he is the propitiation for the sin of both Jews and Gentiles, and not just Jews alone?'

'In the same way, isn't John 3:16 telling us God loved both Jews and Gentiles, and gave his Son that all who believe might be saved?'

'Finally, this could also be the meaning of Paul in 2 Corinthians 5:19, when he speaks of Christ reconciling the world to himself — not that he is reconciling every individual man and woman to himself, but both Jews and Gentiles.'

Our conclusion was that if we were to take the word 'world' in these passages (except John 3:16) to refer to every man and woman on earth, this would be tantamount to universalism, which the Bible definitely does not teach.

For example, to say that Christ is the Saviour of the world (John 4:41-42; 1 John 4:14), in the sense of every man and woman, would be universalism. Or if he is the Lamb of God who takes away the sin of the world (John 1:29) in the sense of every person, this again is universalism. Similarly, if 'He is the propitiation for our sins, and not for ours only, but also for the whole world' (1 John 2:2) means that he is the propitiation for the sins of every individual man and woman in the world, this is universalism. Or if Christ is reconciling the world to himself in the sense of everyone in the world (2 Corinthians 5:19), this again is universalism.

It seemed clear to us, in view of other Bible passages which disprove universalism, that the writers in these passages must be speaking of both Jews and Gentiles when they use the word 'world'.

1. 'This is indeed the Christ, the Saviour of the world [Gentiles, as well as Jews]' (John 4:41-42).
2. 'We have seen and testify that the Father has sent the Son as Saviour of the world [both Jews and Gentiles]' (1 John 4:14).
3. 'Behold! The Lamb of God who takes away the sin of the world [both Jews and Gentiles]!' (John 1:29).
4. 'He ... is the propitiation for our sins [the Jews'], and not for ours only but also for the whole world [both Jews and Gentiles]' (1 John 2:2).
5. 'God was in Christ reconciling the world [both Jews and Gentiles] to Himself' (2 Corinthians 5:19).

We agreed we hadn't solved all the problem passages relating to a limited atonement, but felt we had made progress. We spent the remainder of our time praying and talking about First Baptist Church. I had set in my mind a date (the next day) as the time when I had to make a decision as to what I should do! I was beginning to admit the growing conviction that First Baptist Church would soon have a new pastor!

25.
Time to move on?

As I finally retired that Friday night, I was aware of something else nagging at my mind besides the doctrinal enquiry we were conducting. Knowing that the next day I would tell the chairman of the First Baptist Church pulpit committee that God had given me the same conviction they already had, I wondered if I was hiding something very important from them. I remembered how I had told the pulpit committee at Lime Creek I was not a Calvinist when I didn't even know what one was, something for which I had to repent. Now I wondered if I was wrong in not telling the pulpit committee at First Baptist Church that I was moving in the direction of Calvinistic theology.

Many questions ran through my mind about the matter. What difference does it make to them whether I'm a Calvinist or not? Would they even know what one was? Why imperil my ministry there by telling them I'm something which they don't even understand? Or what if they have only incorrect connotations of the term 'Calvinist', or have only run into unbalanced, extreme Calvinists, and therefore they would immediately place me in the same camp with the over-zealous brothers?

On the other side, did I not owe it to the church (at least to the pulpit committee) to inform them of my views, lest I be accused later of concealing the matter from them? But, again, was I really a Calvinist? I had told them earlier in the disastrous afternoon meeting, fuelled by Dr Bloom's accusation, that I was not a Calvinist, which was an honest answer then. But now I had worked through the first three points of Calvinism and had discovered I was in agreement with the first two (total depravity and unconditional election). On the third, limited atonement, which was the most difficult of the five, I had set down clear convictions which were leaning strongly in that direction. I was beginning to see how the last two (irresistible grace and perseverance of the saints) would follow logically in order from the first three. But still, these two points must be checked in Scripture.

Finally, there was the question whether Calvinism would make any difference in my conducting the work of the ministry. Were my present methods of ministry so far out of line with Calvinistic practice? What, if anything, was I doing which would have to change, were I to embrace fully all the five points of Calvinism?

I suppose the key question was, how much does a prospective pastor tell a future church about his theology and methods of ministry? I could see some real problems if a church was very strong in a particular theological position or strongly committed to certain methods, and a man did not share the same convictions, but did not tell them so.

I could also see some problems (perhaps fewer in this instance), if a man was dogmatic in his views of theology and the methods to be adopted, and the church was not. How serious this was had to depend partly on whether a pastor was willing to go into a church and meet the people where they were theologically, and lead them slowly to his own convictions by the teaching of the Word of God. Was he willing to preach through books of the Bible, expounding them as he went and dealing with these subjects in their biblical context, or would he go in like a bull in a china shop to preach little else than doctrinal sermons on the five points of Calvinism? Again, would he go in loving his people and pastoring them, or would he go in with a chip on his shoulder, daring them to disagree with his preaching and doctrine?

I remembered, at this point, seeing a curriculum vitae prepared by the former pastor at Lime Creek. In it he had set forth in no uncertain terms and at some length that he was a five-point Calvinist, and he not only stated the five points, but thoroughly defined them, along with quotations from the historic confessions supporting his convictions. It appeared to be more of a doctrinal statement than a c.v.

He also stated in this document that God had not called him to visit the sick or the elderly, etc., but to study, pray and preach. I understood his concern to remove the minister from being so taken up in social activities that he spent little time in the study of the Word. I also understood his burden for the minister to take seriously the preparation of sermons, giving this priority a large chunk of his time each week. But, I could also see how someone reading a c.v which was so taken up with doctrine and methods could get a wrong impression.

Finally, I drifted off to sleep, aware that the man who has the problems often does not have the answers, while the man who has the answers probably does not have the problems anyway!

The next morning, a Saturday, I rang the chairman of the pulpit committee at First Baptist Church and told him of my growing conviction concerning coming as pastor. He reacted with a spirit of rejoicing which really encouraged my heart. I mentioned there was one final question that I must ask. His spirit was dampened for a moment until I reassured him that the question was not major, at least from my perspective. We agreed to meet for lunch and discuss any final details, including my question, before I gave a final 'yes'.

I decided that the way to approach the subject when we met was not to ask bluntly, 'Does it make any difference to the church if I am a Calvinist?' There was no use waving a 'red flag' word which could be misunderstood. So when we met, and when we were well into lunch, I asked, 'Does it make any difference what theological persuasion your pastor would hold?'

He answered, 'Well, yes, he would have to be a Baptist.'

I replied, 'Yes, but Baptists today have a variety of theological viewpoints. Historically Baptists have been Calvinistic, but many today have left that persuasion to move to a modified position, even close to Arminianism. The Arminian influence is so great today that many Baptists have never heard of Calvinism, and when they do, they think it is some new heresy, rather than understanding it is historical Baptist theology.'

The puzzled look on his face told me he was not theologically informed of the issues these words stood for; and to be honest, I had no desire to give a theology lesson over lunch. So I gave a general and lengthy, but simple reply.

I told him my theology had been deepening in its understanding in the last several months, and I was sure (even hopeful) that his would continue to grow and mature in the years to come. I told him further that if there ever came a time (which I did not anticipate) when my views were no longer in line with Baptist theology, either past or present, I would resign as pastor.

I also informed him that my main concern was to preach the Word of God in an expository manner, and that if there were any deep theological problems in the text as I moved through a book of the Bible I would deal with them with love and concern for where the people were, in contrast with where I thought they should be according to the Word of God.

I also told him that if my growth in theology produced any convictions concerning a need for a change in the methods adopted in my ministry, I would move slowly in introducing such a change, understanding the need to educate the people about the reasons for the change.

He indicated that these proposals were fine with him!

When I asked him if he thought I should share these convictions with the entire pulpit committee, he said he could assure me that these items would make no difference to them whatsoever. But I insisted I should be allowed to discuss them with the entire pulpit committee. Next, I listed these items, asked him to read them, and then asked him to set up a time when I could present the short document to the entire pulpit committee.

As he had assured me, these issues made no difference to the entire committee, but I sensed in my open discussions with them that my concerns in these areas gave them even a greater love and respect for me. Perhaps they had suffered in the past at the hands of 'lone ranger type' pastors, who had no concern to meet the people where they were, or even to keep them informed as to the reason for changes.

Thus, the decision was finally made! I resigned from Lime Creek Baptist the next Sunday and began making plans to take up the leadership of First Baptist Church of Collegetown. What had seemed so impossible a short time ago had come true! My only reservations concerned what future battles might have to be fought with Dr Bloom.

26.
Does 'all' always mean all?

With the matter of a change in pulpits and churches settled, Terry and I could again concentrate on our theological search. True, I had to make certain preparations for the coming switch, but I had four weeks to bring my ministry at Lime Creek to a close. As Terry and I resumed our study, I reviewed briefly the status of our examination of the third point of Calvinism.

On the one hand, we had seen that *certain verses teach that Christ died for the church in a unique manner*, and this is confirmed by a consideration of the meaning of the word 'atonement'. On the other hand, *certain other verses seem to indicate that he died for all men in the same manner*.

Having established the first proposition as biblical, we had been considering the second set of verses. We had noted that certain ones contained the word 'world'. After considering that the word 'world' in these passages could not possibly mean 'every man', we had concluded that (especially in the light of the historical setting of the early church) 'world' must mean both Jews and Gentiles, as opposed to Jews alone. To take it in most instances as meaning 'everyone' would be to teach universalism — that is, that all men will be saved.

1 Timothy 4:10. The question was now, where should we begin with all these other verses? I suggested to Terry that we begin with an easy one, out of the several verses remaining. She was all in favour of that! The verse I had in mind was 1 Timothy 4:10, which we had listed as saying, 'Christ is the Saviour of all men.' I suggested we look at the entire verse, which reads: 'For to this end we both labour and suffer reproach, because we trust in the living God, who is the Saviour of all men, especially of those who believe.'

We began by noting, firstly, that *this verse does not in fact refer to Christ*! It says 'the living God' (see Matthew 16:16); in other words, God the Father is the one doing something here for all men. Secondly, *this verse does not refer to salvation* either. Rather it is referring to God as the Preserver (one of the meanings of the Greek word translated 'Saviour') of all men, especially of the ones who believe.

Thus the meaning of the verse is that God the Father (the living God) preserves and guards the lives of all men, and believers are especially under the care and kindness of God. Therefore, 1 Timothy 4:10 does not teach that Christ died for all men alike.

1 Timothy 2:1-6. Next we turned to a more difficult section of Scripture — 1 Timothy 2:1-6. Verses 3-6 read as follows: 'For this is good and acceptable in the sight of God our Saviour, who desires *all men* to be saved and to come to the knowledge of the truth. For there is one God and one Mediator between God and men, the Man Christ Jesus, who gave himself a ransom for *all*, to be testified in due time.'

We began by concentrating on two key questions which must be answered in understanding the teaching of this passage.

　　1.　Do the words 'all men' in verse 4 mean every single individual man who has ever lived, or will live, without exception?
　　2.　Does the word 'all' in verse 6 mean every single individual man and woman who has ever lived, or will live, without exception?

When I first asked these questions, Terry was shocked! She asked, 'Doesn't all mean all — full stop? Wouldn't we be playing word games and forcing the Scripture if we tried to make "all" mean something besides all? "All" means all without exception — full stop! Isn't that always the meaning of "all"?'

She sounded quite emphatic, and I thought we might clash for the first time in our study. But then she burst out laughing and I knew she was playing devil's advocate. But still, I had to give her an answer. Does the word 'all' mean 'all men without exception' every time it is used in Scripture?

As before in our search, I had done some initial study so that I could be ready to guide our thinking. On the basis of this study, I put forward the idea that every use of the word 'all' in the Bible does not mean every person without exception. Terry's reaction was to roll her eyes in such a way I wasn't sure if she was still playing devil's advocate, or if she was really sceptical of what I was saying. I was almost convinced it was a sceptical reaction when she challenged me to show her where!

I told her to turn to Mark 1:5 and read it out: 'And *all* the land of Judea, and those from Jerusalem, went out to him and were *all* baptized by him in the Jordan River, confessing their sins.'

I asked her to look at the verse very carefully. Then I went on: 'Does this verse mean that every person, every single individual man and woman from the land of Judea and Jerusalem went out to hear John the Baptist preach? Does it mean that every person, every single individual man and woman from Jerusalem and Judea was baptized in the Jordan River, confessing their sins?'

Terry smiled and admitted, 'You've got me there! No, it can't mean every person or every single individual man and woman.'

'Then,' I queried, 'the Bible does not mean every person, or every single individual, every time it uses the word "all", whatever the context?'

She nodded, tipping her head forward and then backward, not saying a word.

'All right,' I continued, 'now look at these other verses as well.'

I read out: 'Early in the morning He came again into the temple, and *all* the people came to Him; and He sat down and taught them' (John 8:2). I asked her, 'Does "all" in this verse mean every person without exception?'

Her answer again was a silent one — this time a negative shake of the head.

So I read again, this time several verses in a row:

'For you [Paul] will be His witness to *all men* of what you have seen and heard' (Acts 22:15).

'And you will be hated by *all* for my name's sake' (Matthew 10:22).

'And they came to John, and said to him, "Rabbi, He who

was with you beyond the Jordan, to whom you have testified —
behold, He is baptizing, and *all* are coming to Him!' (John 3:26).

I repeated my question again: 'According to these verses, does
the word "all", every time it is used in the Bible, mean every person
without exception?'

Terry didn't answer directly this time — not even her usual nod
or shake of the head. Instead she blurted out in some perplexity,
'What does "all" mean, then, in these verses?' It was not a question
of disagreement, but a genuine query.

I told her 'all' could mean one of two things, or it was used in one
of two ways. Either it was being used in a hyperbolical sense (that
is, 'all' refers to a very large number, but not every person without
exception), or it was used to speak of all men *without distinction,*
that is, it refers to men of all nationalities, generations and classes.

Terry thought about it for a moment and then asked a question:
'It appears obvious that the word "all" does not mean every person
without exception in the verses you've just read. But how do you
know it doesn't bear that meaning in our 1 Timothy 2:4 passage?'

I hadn't thought this whole argument out step by step, but was
thinking it through as I bounced it off Terry.

I replied, 'It seems to me that you would need to search out two
things. First, does the context give any help? Second, does the Bible
anywhere use the phrase "all men" to refer undeniably to every
person without exception?'

Therefore we considered first the thought-flow of the context of
1 Timothy 2.

> *Verse 1.* Paul exhorts them to do several things, but first, that
> supplications, prayers, intercessions and giving of thanks, be
> made on behalf of 'all men'. What is the meaning of 'all' here
> — every person without exception, or every class of persons?
> Obviously, it could not mean every person without exception,
> because they did not know every person on earth without
> exception, and time would not allow them to pray for every man
> on earth without exception. Therefore, it must mean everyone
> in the sense of every class of persons.
>
> *Verse 2.* Paul's exhortation to pray for 'all' men includes
> kings and all those in authority, so that believers may lead a quiet
> and peaceable life in all godliness and reverence. This verse

shows the meaning of 'all' men in verse 1 to be every class of persons, as kings are cited here as one class of many individuals.

Verse 3 Paul tells us we are to pray for all men so that a peaceful and quiet life may result, because this is good and acceptable in the sight of God our Saviour.

Verse 4 Paul states that God desires (not wills in the sense of decrees, or it would take place) all men to be saved and to come to a knowledge of the truth. Again, what is the meaning of 'all' here — every person without exception or every class of persons? The context of verses 1-3 gives clear guidance to understand 'all men' as meaning all classes or orders of men, and not every man without exception.

Verse 5 Paul goes on to state that there is one mediator between God and man, the man Christ Jesus.

Verse 6 Paul designates Christ as the one who gave himself as a ransom on behalf of all men. Again, the previous context of verses 1-4 gives guidance as to the meaning of 'all'. It again refers to classes or orders of men, and Paul is saying that since we are to pray for all orders or classes of men, there is no order or class which is shut out from the gospel.

Therefore, our conclusion was that 1 Timothy 2:1-6 does not teach that Christ died, or made atonement, for all men without exception.

Glancing at my watch in disbelief, I asked Terry if it was really 1 a.m. She laughed and teased, 'Time flies when you're having fun!' To which I added (as I kissed her goodnight), 'And when you're studying the Word of God.'

I headed for the door telling Terry I would ring her the next day. Little did I realize that the next day would not allow me any time to keep my promise!

27.
A blockade

I rose the next morning intending to move my belongings into the First Baptist Church manse. The loading of my few earthly possessions into a borrowed van went without a hitch, but their unloading took me all day, and more — but not by any choice of mine!

When I arrived at the church's manse, I found a group of people blocking the front door. I could not imagine who they were or what they were doing. There were about a hundred of them. I had never seen any of them before.

When I asked them who they were and what they were doing, they informed me they were members of the First Baptist Church who were opposed to my coming as pastor. This information led to a series of questions and answers:

'Were any of you present when I preached at First Baptist Church?'

'No!'

'Were any of you present when the church voted to call me as pastor?'

'No!'

'Do any of you know me or my ministry?'

'No, not exactly.'

'Then, why are you opposed to my coming as pastor?'

'We just don't think you're the man for our church!'

'Why not?'

Their answer to this question was beyond belief, as they replied, 'We're not free to say.'

I repeated, 'Why not?'

'Because you and others would not understand,' they countered. I continued to ask questions.

'Does Dr Bloom have anything to do with this?'

'We can't answer that!'

'How long since you people were active in attendance and support of the church?'

Their answers varied. For some it had been a few years, for others a little longer, or not so long.

'What are your intentions just now?' I queried.

'To stop you from moving into our manse!' they stated emphatically.

My first inclination at this confrontation was to challenge them by beginning the unloading process. But I remembered from my high school days of playing football, that at times it's better to manoeuvre to get a better field position than to challenge a defence when pinned down in the wrong place on the field. So, I got into the van and drove off — straight towards Dr Bloom's house.

Perplexing questions plagued me as I drove. Could Dr Bloom really be behind this? What if I confronted him with what was taking place and he wasn't? What about his recent heart attack? Whether he was or wasn't behind it, wouldn't a confrontation be hazardous to his recovery?

Such thoughts convinced me I should not face Dr Bloom alone. Really, it was not just my problem anyway, but the pulpit committee and fifty members were involved also. Wisely, I stopped and phoned the chairman of the committee. He agreed to go with me to see Dr Bloom.

Initially when Mrs Bloom opened the door, she refused to let us in to see her husband. Finally, we heard a gruff order from within to let us in. We found Dr Bloom lying on the couch in his dressing gown and slippers. I didn't wait for the chairman of the pulpit committee to speak, but asked as humbly and as calmly as I could (under such circumstances), 'Dr Bloom, do you have any idea why we're here?'

His reply was frank and even shocking, as he said, 'Yes, there's a group of First Baptist Church members trying to keep you from moving into our manse.'

My next question was pointless because he had already answered it, but I guess it was more of a numb reaction to his statement. I blurted out, 'Then you know all about this movement?'

'Know about it?' he countered with a smile. 'I organized it! We're just trying to save you the trouble of moving in and then out again later.'

It was obvious that Dr Bloom was enjoying this encounter. Before I could answer he continued, 'Mr Pointer, only about fifty members of First Baptist Church voted to call you as pastor. Actually, this church has two thousand members. The one hundred at the manse are just a small percentage of the overall membership. Is it fair that just fifty out of two thousand should determine who will be the pastor?'

I hardly let him finish before I asked, 'But are these people active members? It seems to me that only the active members should have a right to determine the life and future of the church!'

Dr Bloom spoke condescendingly to me again: 'Young man, this church has no active or inactive membership list. All members are in the same category. There is nothing in our constitution and rules of practice, or in the minutes of past business meetings, that debars any member from the privilege of voting. And at the next regular business meeting, I assure you, many of them will be present to reverse the previous vote which called you as pastor. So save yourself the trouble and don't move in today — you'll never be allowed to stay.'

My reply was bold and contained a rebuke: 'Dr Bloom, I realize what you are doing is no doubt well within the bounds of legality, but I do question the ethical and moral status of your actions. Furthermore, you should be careful, for it may be a case of fighting against God and his will for this church!'

With these words, I excused myself and we made our way back to the house. There I told the crowd that I knew Dr Bloom was behind their movement, but I had prayed about the matter, as had the active members of First Baptist Church, and we were convinced we had found God's will. I warned them of the severe consequences which could come from their opposing the will of God. Furthermore, I told them that to keep me from moving into the manse, they would have to stay for weeks to come, for though I might leave now, I would be back. And when I found no one present, I would move in whether it was night or day.

Having uttered these convictions, we left and went to eat lunch, and then returned to the house to find the blockade gone! I spent the rest of the afternoon and evening moving in and straightening up. It wasn't until I wearily crawled into bed in my new house that evening that I remembered I had not rung Terry.

And though I was utterly weary in body and mind, I came to some conclusions about the typical Baptist church. I saw that most were like First Baptist Church — filled with inactive members who still had a right to vote. It was shocking to realize that at any time this large group could enter the church and vote to do just about anything they wished — even turn the church into a public house if they wanted to. I was convinced something had to be done in all churches with similar situations!

I wondered how Baptist churches ever got into such a mess! Don't all practical matters in a church, good or bad, have a doctrinal basis? In other words, theology is not something we simply believe but which is unrelated to our practices; rather, our practices are the result of what we believe. If Baptist churches are in such a mess today, then it must be traced to what they believe. You cannot separate practical theology from doctrinal theology. When doctrinal theology goes astray, then practical theology will follow. You cannot have a strong and correct practical theology without a strong and correct doctrinal theology. And if Baptist practices of the day are so questionable, what, I wondered, does that say about their theology?

28.
For everyone or everything?

The next few weeks I was so busy with the closing of one ministry and the beginning of another that Terry and I didn't have much time for theologizing. Then, also, because it was summer, holiday time was upon us, and Terry was out of town for several days in the midst of the move.

The first Sunday at First Baptist Church as their pastor went very well. Dr Bloom was not present and neither were any of the inactive members that he was stirring up. The faithful fifty who did attend were overwhelmingly encouraging to their new young pastor and his preaching. But I realized there was a threatening cloud hanging over us — the next business meeting when Dr Bloom and his inactive majority would move in and try to take over. We began to make that meeting a definite matter of continual prayer. We realized our God was our only hope, if we were to avoid a very painful confrontation. Clearly, there was no way, humanly speaking, whereby fifty active members could outvote several hundred (the potential was two thousand, according to Dr Bloom) inactive members.

The following Friday evening found us once more at Terry's, still wrestling with the subject of limited, or particular, atonement. We had dealt with enough verses to realize that the usual interpretations of passages which were supposed to teach general atonement did not stand up to close examination. But several other important passages remained and laid upon us the necessity of careful scriptural examination and answers.

Hebrews 2:9. This evening we began with Hebrews 2:9, which reads as follows: 'But we see Jesus, who was made a little lower than the angels, for the suffering of death crowned with glory and honour, that He, by the grace of God, might taste death for everyone.'

I had to admit that this verse seemed convincing — Christ tasted death for everyone. But I had been taking Greek in my first two years at college, and had even developed a procedure to use it in my sermon preparation. I had seen many times the light which the original language brought to the understanding of Scripture.

As I looked at the passage and its context, I noticed something very interesting — that there was a Greek word *(pas)* in its various forms used throughout verses 8-10: '"You have put *all things [panta]* in subjection under his feet." For in that He put *all [ta panta]* in subjection under him, He left nothing that is not put under him. But now we do not yet see *all things [ta panta]* put under him. But we see Jesus ... that He, by the grace of God, might taste death for *everyone [huper pantos —* note also the Greek word *anthropos* for man is not in this verse.] For it was fitting for Him, for whom are *all things [ta panta]*, and by whom are *all things [ta panta]* ...'

Realizing that Terry didn't know the Greek language, I wrote down the alternative ways in which each of these phrases could be translated in the light of the gender used in the Greek.

Either: 'You have put *all men* in subjection under his feet,'
or: 'You have put *all things* in subjection under his feet.'

Either, 'For in that he put *all men* in subjection under him,'
or:'For in that he put *all things* in subjection under him.'

Either:'But now we do not yet see *all men* put under him,'
or: 'But now we do not yet see *all things* put under him.'

Either: '... that He, by the grace of God, might taste death for *everyone,'*
or: '... that He, by the grace of God, might taste death for *everything'.*

Either: 'For it was fitting for Him, for whom are *all men* and by whom are *all men...'* or, 'For it was fitting for Him, for whom are *all things* and by whom are *all things...'*

Obviously, to interpret the passage, we had to answer the following questions: Should we translate this Greek word as 'all things' and 'everything' throughout? Or should we translate this Greek word as 'all men' and 'everyone' throughout? Or again, should we translate this passage 'all things' (everything) in some places and 'all men' (everyone) in other places? What it came down to was, should we translate this form as a masculine or a neuter (the form in the Greek can be either) whenever it is used in this passage?

It seemed to us that the context was very important here. So we summarized the thought-flow of the passage:

God made Christ a little lower than the angels.
God crowned Christ with glory and honour.
God set Christ over the works of creation (v. 7).
God has put all things in subjection under his feet.
In putting all things in subjection to him, God left nothing removed from under his authority (v. 8).
But we see Jesus made a little lower than the angels for the suffering of death, crowned with glory and honour, that he, by the grace of God, might taste death [here is the problem] for everything, or for everyone (v. 9).
Because it was fitting for him, for whom are all things and by whom are all things, in bringing many sons to glory, to make the author of their salvation perfect through suffering (v. 10).

The argument of the passage seemed to flow as follows:

1. God made Christ a little lower than the angels (that is, in the form of a man), and set him over all things of his creation.
2. But now (due to sin) not all things are under him.
3. But by his death there will be a benefit to the whole creation, as he tasted death for everything. By this death he would bring many sons to glory.

This interpretation agrees with Romans 8:19-22, where Paul says, 'For the earnest expectation of the creation eagerly waits for the revealing of the sons of God. For the creation was subjected to futility, not willingly, but because of Him who subjected it in hope; because the creation itself also will be delivered from the bondage of corruption into the glorious liberty of the children of God. For we know that the whole creation groans and labours with birth pangs together until now.'

Even if we were to take Hebrews 2:7-8 to refer to men, and not to Christ, the message is the same: God made man a little lower than the angels and crowned him with glory and honour. God set man over the works of God's creation — all the works of God's creation. But now (due to sin) not all things are under man's authority. Therefore to bring all things under man's authority, we see Jesus taking on the form of man for the suffering of death for everything, and through this death he will also bring many sons to glory. The point of the passage is that Christ's death not only brings many sons to glory, but also removes the curse of sin from God's creation.

At this point of our consideration, the phone rang, something unusual for our Friday night meetings. Terry answered, and then handed it over to me, mouthing softly, 'It's Todd, and he's excited.'

His excitement stemmed from a phone-call he had received from the Lime Creek Baptist Church's pulpit committee. They wanted to talk to him about the possibility of his becoming a candidate for the pastorate of their church.

I rejoiced with him and then teased him, 'What are you going to tell them if they ask you if you are a Calvinist?'

29.
A test of faith

As the hour of the fearful, and possibly fatal, business meeting drew near, when the inactive members would rally in full force to vote me out, I found a peaceful spirit settling upon the church. I addressed them the previous Sunday on the subject of prayer, stressing that the proper spirit and attitude of prayer must be a sense of helplessness, hopelessness even, if the matter depended on us. Then we joined together in prayer and declared in tears our helplessness and put the matter fully into God's hands. We organized to pray around the clock between midnight on that Sunday night and the seven o'clock prayer meeting on Wednesday.

I also mulled over in my mind the possible actions I could take to stop the takeover attempt. I had thought about cancelling the meeting but that would only be putting off the inevitable. I had considered passing a resolution on the Sunday evening prior to the regular Wednesday business meeting that would have declared that only active members could hold voting privileges! I realized that this action should probably have been taken months ago, but it was out of the question on such short notice according to the church's constitution and rules of practice. And besides, what majority of inactive members would deny themselves voting privileges? All other ideas I came up with were in the same categories — either putting off the inevitable or constitutionally or practically impossible. I concluded that we were shut up completely to the Lord and his working on our behalf. I also began to wonder about the salvation of such people. Could they truly be the elect of God?

On Tuesday evening as I was eating a late supper (snack would be a better word, since I had prepared it myself), the phone rang, and to my surprise it was Mrs Bloom. She spoke briskly and to the point, saying, 'Dr Bloom would like to see you.'

I wanted to say, 'Let him come to the manse. I'll be here all evening!' But that seemed out of place in the light of his health and of the need for me to be seen to react in a Christian way. I had discovered as a pastor that other people in the church could act in very un-Christlike ways and few would fault them for it. But let the pastor be petty or small or unchristian in his actions on just one occasion, and people would hang him for it! What others could get away with in bad actions, the pastor could not.

So, instead of telling Dr Bloom to come to me, I asked, 'Mrs Bloom, can you tell me what he wishes to see me about?' It was an unnecessary question in that I was sure I already knew the answer, but it was necessary to keep the conversation going.

'He wants to see you about the meeting at church tomorrow night!' she replied.

'I'll be along in about an hour,' I told her.

Dr Bloom was his usual self when I arrived — not in the room. Mrs Bloom escorted me to his study, and the usual wait ensued. I looked upon it as his psychological play to frighten or intimidate me. Finally, his wife wheeled him into the room and the battle of wits began.

After the usual formalities and greeting, I waited for him to speak.

'Mr Pointer, you know you will be voted out as pastor of First Baptist Church tomorrow night, don't you?' he asked.

'No,' I replied, 'I don't know that.'

He was taken aback and asked, 'Where do you think you will get enough people to counter the vote we will bring in? We have between 100-200 people who have pledged to be present for the vote. You have only about fifty to stand by you.'

My reply may have sounded super-spiritual, but it was the truth: 'Dr Bloom, my trust for the coming meeting is not in men, nor numbers of men, but in the Lord. He will determine the outcome.'

That really annoyed him! 'Mr Pointer,' he growled, 'I called you here this evening hoping you would be wise and open to counsel and even to a compromise. I'm suggesting that you open the meeting on

Wednesday by offering your resignation, and our group will follow by voting you six months pay for your move to restore unity to the church. Don't you think that is a fair offer?'

Once more he was totally unprepared for my answer. 'Dr Bloom,' I began boldly, 'here's my ultimatum! Either you cease and desist from your rebellious actions, or you will have to answer to God—not me. The Bible says, "Rebellion is as the sin of witchcraft, and stubbornness is as iniquity and idolatry"! (1 Samuel 15:23). Dr Bloom, I don't think you would be caught dead dabbling in witchcraft or idolatry, but you are guilty of rebellion and stubbornness! I fear for you and for your health, and even for your life if you persist in this action! If you have any deals to make, make them with God, not me, but I'm sure you know any dealings with him must be preceded by confession and repentance of sin! I think that's all we have to say to one another. Thank you, I will show myself to the door!'

As I made my way down the hall towards the front door, I heard him call out, 'Mr Pointer, don't you walk out on me. I've not finished with you! You can't treat your superior that way.'

But I was acting with a purpose: I wanted to leave him not only with a declaration of strong truth, but with the impression of my faith and determination not to give in to his intriguing.

As I drove home praying, I thought to myself, 'This time tomorrow the matter will be settled!' And it was at this moment that the practicality of Calvinism struck me. Was it really true that God was sovereign in all things — even in the negative events and experiences of our lives? I had to answer yes, in the light of my search during the past few months. And I found a sweet comfort as I knew at this moment that my God was in control of all the events of my life, the one working all things in my life after the counsel of his own will — even my ministry at the First Baptist Church. The enemy could not do anything my God had not decreed from eternity past. I was there as pastor as long as he willed, and I would not want to be there any longer — not even past tomorrow evening.

30.
'Will you take the funeral?'

I don't know for certain how long I had been asleep on the Tuesday night after my confrontation with Dr Bloom, when the jangling of the phone brought me to my senses.

I was barely awake when I heard the voice on the other end of the line say, 'Rev. Pointer, this is Mrs Bloom. Dr Bloom wants to see you right away!'

Wearily I protested, 'Mrs Bloom, we've been through all of that earlier this evening and...'

But she interrupted, not letting me finish, 'He's back in the hospital — he suffered another heart attack about two hours after you left tonight. He wants you to come — seriously.'

I could not help but say, 'Don't you think my coming could aggravate his condition, and make him worse?'

'No, I think he has truly had a change of mind and heart! I want you to know, Rev. Pointer, that I never agreed with his wish to keep you from pastoring our church. I stand behind you and now I am certain he will too.'

Without further ado, I told her, 'I'll be there in a few minutes.'

When I walked into the hospital room, the place was buzzing with activity as doctors and nurses were working frantically. Mrs Bloom quickly saw me and softly said, 'I'm afraid he's gone. Just after I rang you, he had another bad turn.'

Tears were streaming down her face. I put my arm around her to comfort her, and she said again quietly, 'Thanks for coming.' We stood there together until one of the doctors turned to us and told us sadly, 'It's too late — he's gone.' How wonderful it would have

been to talk with him just once more to witness his change of mind
— but that was not to be!

As I sought to comfort Mrs Bloom, she made a request for which
I was totally unprepared: 'Rev. Pointer, will you take his funeral?'

I tried to tell her I would be glad to do so, but surely, there must
be others — a former pastor, a fellow teacher or administrator at
college, or a close friend in the ministry.

She replied firmly but sweetly, 'This is not just my wish, but it
was what Dr Bloom wanted, and I agree with it. After you left this
evening, Dr Bloom and I had a long talk. For the first time in this
episode of his obsession to remove you from the pastorate of our
church, I spoke my mind. I told him you were right in everything you
had said tonight! I told him that in all our years together, I had never
known him to be so wrong. For a few minutes he just sat and stared
at the wall in a sullen, irritated manner. Then he broke down in tears
and admitted I was right and he had been a stubborn, rebellious fool.
He planned to phone you tomorrow and apologize. Then when the
attack came, he seemed to know that these were his last hours. He
made me promise that if anything happened, I would pass on to you
his apology, and that I would ask and urge you to preach at the
funeral. So, will you take the service, please?'

I assured her I would be glad to do so! Then she said, 'And don't
worry about tonight! I will inform the inactive movement that their
work is over, and if any of them insist on going through with the
action, I will be there tonight to speak out against them, and even tell
them Dr Bloom's last wishes on this matter.'

The Wednesday night business meeting was as normal as any I
had ever led! None of the inactive members turned up to carry out
their purpose. No doubt they were deeply shocked, not only by the
news of the death of their leader, but also of his last-minute change
of mind and heart. We spent most of the time in praise and
thanksgiving for God's providential working on our behalf, as I
shared with the membership the details of the previous evening.
They had all heard something, but did not know the particulars. But
our hearts were sad over Dr Bloom's passing, especially at the
moment when the Lord had moved upon his heart.

The funeral service also went well — as funeral services go. I
said nothing about Dr Bloom's opposition to me or the church.
Rather, I spoke of his years of faithful service for the Lord. My

actions of love and compassion endeared me to Mrs Bloom's heart and I knew I had gained a faithful lifelong supporter of my ministry at First Baptist Church.

My greatest sorrow was that I had not got to know Dr Bloom as a friend after his resentment and opposition to me had been resolved. He could have been such a great help to me personally as well as to my ministry!

31.
Todd gets carried away

The weeks that followed the death of Dr Bloom were packed with busy activity. The autumn term of my third year at college began; the responsibility of pastoral duties continued to mount; and new problems began to emerge with Todd!

He had been called to the pastorate of Lime Creek Baptist Church. We had been meeting regularly to discuss the ministry and biblical truth, but when he became pastor, he moved into the manse and began to travel back and forth to college. This had been going on for several weeks, a couple of months even, when the chairman of the deacons at Lime Creek called me. He said he had to see me.

When I asked why, he said it was about the new pastor and some of his practices. I immediately questioned in my mind the ethics of a former pastor meddling in the affairs of a church where he had previously held the pastorate. I certainly did not want to create division in the church between a pastor and his people, so I tried to explain this to the chairman and to refuse to meet him. But he insisted, telling me the situation at Lime Creek was very serious, and Todd's ministry there and the church's future were at stake. All the blessings of the past few years in the church were in jeopardy. I agreed to meet with him just to listen to the problem, but said I would not get involved.

As we met for lunch that day, the chairman of the deacons told me Todd had become just like Jim Mitchell, the pastor who had preceded me — an offensive, militant Calvinist. It wasn't that this chairman did not know what Calvinism was, for he had been introduced to the doctrine under my ministry. What he told me, I just could not believe.

Todd, so he said, had given up preaching and was giving theological lectures on the five points of Calvinism. He was offensive in his attitude, virtually daring people to disagree with him in his doctrine and preaching. He had dismantled the programme of evangelistic outreach. He told them what had taken place under my ministry was of the flesh — quite a statement, since a number of his church members had been either revived or born again during that period of time. He was using all kinds of terms which many people knew from my teaching and preaching, but for him they had to be constant bywords to test a person's orthodoxy as a Christian and as a minister.

He wanted to change the constitution and rules of practice of the church (not a bad idea in itself, if done for proper reasons, and, indeed, we had made some changes in my time), but one of the changes he wanted to introduce was a requirement that a person be a Calvinist before he or she could be a member.

All of this was being proposed by a man who had been pastor of the church for just a few weeks!

I asked the deacon friend where Todd was getting such ideas, as I could not imagine him doing anything like this on his own. The reply was that he and Jim Mitchell had become staunch friends, and the influence came from Jim. He and his family had come back and joined the church, much to the fear and concern of all the membership. Todd was promoting him to teach the major Sunday school class! The deacon's obvious question was, 'What shall we do?'

I had to confess I did feel a little responsible for the situation because I had introduced the doctrine to Todd, and I had also encouraged the church to call him as pastor; and because of my busy schedule, I had not made any great effort to keep in contact with him since he moved to live near the church. We had discussed doctrine in great depth, and I had warned him of the dangers of extremism and falling into hyper-Calvinism, but evidently the former pastor had taken advantage of the fact that Todd was a follower, and had greatly influenced him for the worst.

Therefore, I promised the deacon I would re-establish communication with Todd, and give him a chance to tell me what was going on — and perhaps even to seek my counsel and advice —

before I made any attempt to approach him critically or accusingly on the subject.

I sighed deeply as I drove to my own church. If it's not one problem in the ministry, it's another! Or even several at once! How subtly but certainly Satan moves in people's lives! But then I realized that problems are only opportunities for the Lord to work something special and unusual in his own way and by his power. But only faith could understand this, and so be able to rejoice in the face of problems. I prayed for faith to understand and to rejoice even in this situation.

32.
The timing of the Second Coming

That evening, following my conversation with the deacon of Lime Creek, Terry and I got together again to take up our theological discussion. It wasn't that I had not been involved in the search during these weeks since Dr Bloom's death. Rather, I had been wrestling with one of the most difficult of all the passages which were supposed to teach general atonement — 2 Peter 3:9, which stated: 'The Lord is not slack concerning His promise, as some count slackness, but is longsuffering toward us, not willing that any should perish but that all should come to repentance.'

The few times (and it only takes a few) I had sought to have a conversation with anyone about the subject of particular atonement versus general atonement, I had been presented with the quotation of this verse as if it were the final authority on the whole matter, regardless of what the Bible might say in other places. Therefore, I had given the passage a rather thorough study and exegesis, not from what others had said or written, but from my Greek New Testament.

2 Peter 3:9. First, I had listed several questions I needed to ask concerning the usual interpretation of this passage, and these I shared with Terry:

 1. What does this passage teach about God, according to the usual interpretation?
 2. What does this passage teach about the interval until the Second Coming of Christ, according to the usual view?
 3. Who is meant by 'us', according to common understanding of the passage?

4. Is 'any' the proper translation in this passage?
5. To whom does the word 'all' refer in this context?

Next, I proceeded to try to answer these questions according to the usual interpretation, but not necessarily in the order of my listing of them.

I explained to Terry that the usual general atonement interpretation sees this passage as a statement concerning the delay of the Second Coming. According to this view, God has provided an atonement for all men. He is wishing to have all men come to him for salvation. He is not willing that any single person should perish. This stems from his longsuffering attitude to all men. Therefore he is delaying the Second Coming, hoping a few more will be saved before he has to ring down the curtain of time. Maybe they will, and maybe they won't be saved, but God waits patiently, hoping that will allow a few more to go to heaven instead of hell. Whether they will or whether they won't is up to them, and not in accordance with any plan or purpose of God.

Therefore, to answer the questions I had listed earlier in order *according to the common view*, we should have to say,

1. God has done all he can to save men (that is, he has provided an atonement for all), and now he must wait for each one to respond, depending on how each person decides.

2. The interval of time until Christ comes is a period of uncertainty and hope for God. It is a time during which God waits for man's response to his provision, even delaying the Second Coming in the hope of a few more being saved.

3. The 'us' refers to all mankind— 'God is longsuffering to 'us' means to all men.

4. 'Any' is a proper translation.

5. 'all' refers to all men — every individual member of the human race.

I realized the time was flying when I reached this point, but this was not the place to stop in the presentation. Terry had no questions concerning the common viewpoint, so we began to consider the correctness or incorrectness of the usual interpretation.

I decided to begin with the heart of the matter—is *'any'* a correct translation here? That would not settle the whole issue, but would help us understand a common error in handling this passage.

I explained to Terry that the word 'any' was an indefinite pronoun in the Greek, and was to be translated,when it was in the singular form, as 'any' or 'one' or 'a certain one'. But in this verse it is not in the singular form in the original language. It is in the plural, and the plural form is translated as 'ones', or 'some', or 'certain ones', or 'certain men'. I showed her a list of the numerous places where the various plural forms of this word were used in the Greek New Testament. In each place the plural form spoke of more than one person — the obvious purpose of a plural. So if the author of this passage had meant 'any', wouldn't he have used the singular form of the pronoun instead of the plural? Didn't his use of the plural mean that he was speaking of 'some' or 'certain ones'?

Next, I moved to consider the word *'all'* — 'but that all should come to repentance'. I pointed out that the word 'all' stood in a sentence of contrasting phrases. In the same sentence we are first told something concerning which God is not willing, and then, in contrast, we are told of something concerning which God is willing. In the contrast the word 'all' in the second phrase stands in relation to the words 'certain ones' in the first phrase. In other words, 'all' is qualified by the term 'certain ones', referring to them, and them alone. God is not willing that certain ones should perish, but that all of these certain ones should come to repentance. 'All' cannot stand by itself and mean all men, but must be understood in relation to the certain ones already mentioned.

In the light of this understanding, the word 'us' clearly does not refer to all mankind (I noted in passing that the word is 'you' in some manuscripts). Even if it stood alone, how could we make it a reference to all mankind? It speaks of a specific group. Even if we were to adopt the alternative variant reading of 'you', it still speaks of a specific group, and not all mankind.

On the basis of this textual study, I explained to Terry my understanding of the whole passage, under the following points:

1. Some scoffers had raised the question of the delay of the Second Coming. Did that delay mean that God was slack in some way regarding the fulfilment of his promise, maybe even incapable of bringing it to pass? Why the delay?

2. Peter answers that there is a group who are the object of God's forbearance, and God is not willing that these certain ones should perish, but that all of these people should come to repentance.

3. Therefore, the Second Coming is not delayed, but it is right on schedule according to God's plan and purpose in saving a people. Christ will come when this people is complete, and in the interval till then he will work, bringing these people to salvation.

4. Therefore, the passage is not teaching that God is holding up the Second Coming in the hope that all men, or a few more men, will be saved. Rather, the Second Coming will take place according to God's purpose and will, which includes the calling out of a people prior to that time.

5. This interpretation not only is true to the text and context, but it also is true to the biblical concept of God — a God who is in control and who is working all things after the counsel of his own will, rather than a weak God who is manipulated and controlled by man and his will.

We sat and talked about this passage for about another hour or so, but were in agreement concerning the meaning of this verse in the light of these considerations. We marvelled at the way the total revelation of God harmonizes and exalts him — and not man.

33.
Lunch with Todd

The next week I had fully intended to give Todd a ring and see if we could have lunch. I tried a few times but got no answer and, with a busy schedule, Thursday was upon me before I knew it. But then God in his providence brought to pass what I had failed to achieve as I met Todd at college in the morning.

Quickly between classes I suggested we have lunch soon.

He jumped at the suggestion saying, 'What's wrong with today?'

So we arranged to meet a little before noon at one of the local restaurants, and I couldn't help wondering if his suggesting today meant he wanted to talk to me too. Obviously he did (though maybe not about the situation as being a problem), because as we sat down he began to rattle off all the wonderful things the Lord was doing at the church. Maybe he wanted to impress me with the fact that something was taking place since I had left and he had become the pastor.

But even if that was the case it was not spoken in a boastful manner. Clearly, I was not talking to the same old Todd. There was now a soberness and maturity that I had never seen before. Gone was the 'happy-go-lucky' spirit of past days. Absent also was the 'everything-is-funny' attitude for which he had been famous. In fact, he was almost too serious. He appeared to be something of an anachronism — a genuine, full-blooded Puritan, in attitude as well as theology, in the latter part of the twentieth century. I almost expected to hear a 'thee' or a 'thou' come out of his mouth. I saw in him shades of Jim Mitchell.

I was even more convinced of the Mitchell influence when some of the theology and its practical application which Todd mentioned fell short of the biblical standards. He began to tell me that God loved only the elect; that we cannot challenge men to come to Christ in repentance and faith because not all men are of the elect; that we cannot offer the gospel to all men but only to the elect; that most evangelistic efforts are of the flesh; that even what took place during my ministry at Lime Creek was a work of man and not a work of God; that if God wanted the lost saved, he would save them without us; and that he would only fellowship in the future with men of his own persuasion.

I shuddered inwardly as I realized I had a full-blown, extreme Calvinist in front of me — one who could do more damage in a week to the cause of Christ and truth than several dozen true Calvinists could do good in a year. It's no wonder so-called Calvinists have a bad image in some places. Admittedly, even the true Calvinist is misunderstood and maligned at times, but how much fodder a warped Calvinist gives the enemy against the cause of truth!

I knew I had to confront him, but where would I begin? The words just kept rolling out of his mouth and in such seriousness.

Finally I found an opening and plunged in, asking, 'Todd, where in the world are you getting these ideas? Are they your own? Can you truly tell me that you would claim to get these thoughts from the Word of God? If so, where? Have I missed something in my study?'

His answer was very much as I expected, when he told me, 'Brother Mitchell and I have been studying the Bible together, and these are some of the truths God has been teaching us.'

I boldly challenged him: 'Are you sure you've been studying the Word of God together, or has he just been feeding you some of his misinterpretations of the Word?'

For a moment he was silent, as if he realized my question had some truth in it. But then he assured me, it was a joint study they were undertaking together — and that I found hard to believe!

Therefore I told him bluntly, 'Todd, you've always been a follower! Before you were saved you professed that you were saved, but followed a worldly crowd in its thoughts and lifestyle until you made a complete mess of your life, badly hurting other people in the process all along the way. But God in his grace and mercy saved you. He brought you under the lordship of his Son, Jesus Christ. He intended you to follow him and his Word. I taught you, introducing you to many precious truths during those first few months of your salvation, but never once did I desire or seek to take the place of the Holy Spirit or the lordship of Christ in your life! Perhaps, in some ways, you would have liked that, or it would have made life easier in some respects for you. But realizing your weakness and tendency to be a follower, and also because I understood the damage it would bring to make you a little imitation of myself, I sought to point you to Christ and to teach you the place of the Holy Spirit in leading and teaching you the truth about him. But now I see someone else has jumped in to play God in your life and you are allowing it to take place. Let me warn you, that just as being a blind follower of falsehood before you were saved led to heartache for you and others, so if you continue to be a blind follower of another spiritually, it will lead to the same results — heartache for you as well as others! — heartache of the deepest sort!'

As I spoke, I saw a tear beginning to trickle down one cheek. When I finished, he thanked me, and promised he would consider my words, and then we parted.

Mixed emotions again filled me as I drove home. There was no doubt about it — Todd would never have allowed me to talk to him like that before. He would have lost his temper and walked away. The very fact that he had listened and been touched by my words was probably evidence of a regenerate heart, for which I rejoiced. But I was grieved that he did not see the need to break with Jim Mitchell for his own and the church's sake. I could only pray and wait for the Lord to turn this trouble into blessing.

34.
'The Lord who bought them'

All in my life, at this point at least, was not discouraging, as were the unwelcome changes I had seen in Todd. The ministry at First Baptist Church was clearly showing the hand of God upon it. The people (that is, the faithful few) were growing in the Lord and rejoicing in what God was teaching them. Even some of the inactive members had returned and were showing signs of true salvation and growth.

But hanging over the church continually was the fact that the membership still included hundreds of those who showed no signs of regeneration — a group who sat quietly at home like a time-bomb waiting to explode if the church were to seek to do anything with which they did not agree. All they needed was a leader and a cause, and they could come in and vote to do anything they wanted.

I knew something had to be done about them, but what? If we held a meeting to put them on an inactive list, they could come and not only defeat the vote, but in anger vote in whatever they wanted. If we held a meeting to remove them from the membership of the church, they could come and not only defeat that vote, but also vote the pastor and the godly element out of the church. I sensed the need not to disturb the slumbering giant until the Lord definitely led.

This convinced me all the more of the need for true evangelism, for surely it had been a false evangelism which had added many of these people to the church roll without regeneration. I was struck by the obvious inconsistency of people who wanted to be members of the church, and who expected to keep the privilege of voting (though only when it was a volatile issue), but never wanted to shoulder any of the responsibilities of the church in attendance, working, giving, and so on. It was also obvious that these people could not have any kind of spiritual understanding, to know God's will in any matter of the life of the church, if their minds were cold and indifferent to the Word of God and its teaching and preaching.

I continued to make this a matter of prayer, knowing eventually I must deal with it.

2 Peter 2:1. When Terry and I met for our next session, there was still one verse we wanted to discuss in relation to limited atonement. This was 2 Peter 2:1, which reads, 'But there were also false prophets among the people, even as there will be false teachers among you, who will secretly bring in destructive heresies, even denying the Lord who bought them, and bring on themselves swift destruction ...'

Since this again was a very difficult passage which had required background study, I did most of the talking. I began, as with the last passage we had studied, by stating the usual interpretation of the passage:

1. The word 'Lord' here refers to Jesus Christ.

2. The word 'bought' here refers to redemption through the work of Christ.

3. The passage is therefore seen as teaching that Christ the Lord has bought (paid the redemptive price for, in the form of a general atonement) these false teachers.

4. These false teachers are denying the Lord Jesus, who died to pay the penalty of their sin, which includes a redemption which they have never received, because they are not saved.

5. Therefore Christ must have paid the redemptive price of all men, and each must accept or reject his payment.

We both agreed that over the years we had heard this passage explained in this manner. The only other possibility we had heard even suggested was that some people used this verse to teach a person could lose his salvation, as these false teachers were examples of redeemed persons becoming apostate. But this view was always rejected by Baptists because of the Baptist conviction of 'Once saved — always saved'.

Next I set before Terry some little known facts which usually go unmentioned in the handling of this passage, and these raised the following questions:

1. Does the word 'Lord' here really refer to Christ, especially in view of the fact that the Greek word is not the usual word used to speak of him as Lord *(kurios)*? The word here is *despotes* which, except in one place, is always used in the New Testament to refer either to God the Father or to masters of servants. And in the one place where it is used of Christ, in Jude 4, it is used to speak not of his lordship, but to speak of him as Sovereign. In fact the distinction is clear because both *kurios* and *despotes* are used in this passage.

2. Can the word 'bought' here really refer to a general atonement, in which a price is paid for redemption, but the purchase is not complete because it depends on man's acceptance? This question is necessary in view of the fact that all but five uses of the word in the New Testament speak of a concept of buying, which puts the purchaser in possession of that which he bought. It never speaks of a potential purchase depending on some other factor. In the five exceptions (see 1 Corinthians 6:20; 7:23; Revelation 5:9; 14:3-4) the word is used of redemption, but it never speaks of a potential redemption, but of an accomplished redemption, as those spoken of are saved people.

On the basis of the meaning of these two words, we had to conclude that this passage could not teach a general atonement — that is, that Christ had paid a general redemptive price for all men. The 'Lord' referred to in this passage was not Christ, but God the Father, and the word used here for 'bought', always, in every place where it is used in the New Testament, speaks of a complete purchase which puts the buyer in ownership and possession of the object. It never speaks of a potential purchase, such as suggested in a general atonement.

But if the usual interpretation was not the meaning of the passage, then what did it mean? A clear handling of a passage not only includes recognizing what it does not and cannot say, but also what it does say.

Since two key words ('Lord' and 'bought') had specific meanings, we felt these must give us guidance in determining the meaning of the passage. 'Lord' speaks not of Christ, but of the sovereign God and his authority over all. 'Bought' speaks of a purchase which establishes ownership and authority. The phrase, then, must refer to God in his sovereignty and authority over all, even his ownership and authority over these false teachers.

Thus the tragedy here is not that these false teachers are denying Christ, who paid a general redemptive price for them. Rather the tragedy is that these false teachers are denying the sovereign God who owns them by the right of creation. It would be more consistent, in the light of the meaning of 'bought' (a purchase which results in possession) to interpret the passage to mean that these false teachers are saved men, but then we should have to square that interpretation with all the passages which deny the loss of salvation by a believer.

Clearly these men are 'owned' by God, but not in a redemptive sense, but in their relation to him as the sovereign Creator and Owner of all things. The tragedy is that, as they are owned and sustained by God himself, they are denying him, and all in the name of Christianity.

We concluded that this should not sound strange and impossible, especially in the light of those who were doing the same thing in our day.

35.
Jim is put in his place

I didn't expect to find anyone waiting for me when I arrived home that night after we finished our discussion of 2 Peter 2:1. I was surprised not only at finding someone waiting in the darkness of my porch, but also at the identity of the person who stepped out of the shadows as I was unlocking my door. It was Jim Mitchell.

'We've got to talk!' he stated rather matter-of-factly.

'At this time of night?' I queried.

'Yes, right now!' he insisted. 'It can't wait.'

He came in, and after turning on a light, I motioned for him to sit down in the living room. I bought a little time by going to the cupboard to hang up my coat, seeking to anticipate what he wanted to talk about. I concluded that Todd must have told him of our conversation, including my rebuke, in which I had spoken about Jim in a negative way, and that he was there to argue over the issues I had raised.

As I returned to the living room, he fired the first salvo by saying, 'You had no right to speak to Todd the way you did last week!'

'Are you referring to the manner in which I spoke to him, or to the content of our conversation?' I asked, wishing to clarify the issue which had upset him.

His reply didn't help me much, as he answered, 'Both!'

Seeking to forestall a heated argument at this time of night I simply replied, 'Well, it's obvious we have a difference of opinion on that matter.'

'You had no right to criticize me to Todd,' he insisted. 'And you have no right to interfere in the Lime Creek Baptist Church.'

By now I was convinced there was no quick and easy way out of this confrontation, so I decided I might as well meet him head on. I waded right in by challenging him: 'Jim, you brought great grief to that church as its pastor several years ago by your hyper-Calvinism, and that was bad enough once. But now you're going to bring great grief not only to the church again, but also to a very good friend of mine who not long ago was lost. Did you show any concern for Todd before he was saved? Now that God has saved him, your main concern is to make him into an unbalanced hyper-Calvinist like yourself.'

I was in full flow now, so I didn't even pause to let him answer. 'Jim, there's something I've always wanted to ask a hyper-Calvinist like you. Why is it you have more concern to make people into Calvinists of your own twisted brand than to see lost people come to know Christ Jesus as Lord and Saviour? Why is it you spend all your time and effort on teaching believers they need to be like you, but never spend time or effort to witness to the lost? Why is it your concern for missions and evangelism is next to nothing, but your zeal to make all Christians into Calvinists of your own particular type is consuming and never-ending? Could it be that men like you are the reason some people have the false idea that Calvinism kills evangelism and missions?

'If you ask me, I'd rather a man have a few Arminian tendencies and a burden for a lost world, than be an extreme Calvinist like you, with little or no concern for lost people to come to know Christ. And because of this, I refuse to step aside and let you mislead a dear friend of mine, and even further, to bring grief to a church and people I dearly love.'

I wanted to say more, but felt I had already said enough, maybe even too much. I waited to see how he would answer.

His manner was condescending and his eyes blazed as he said, 'Ira, I've always known you were not a true Calvinist! Now what you have just said proves it.' He paused for me to answer, so I did.

'Well, if being a true Calvinist means I must deny the Christian and the church the responsibility they have for missions and evangelism, then I am not a true Calvinist!

'If it means refusing to challenge the lost with their responsibility to believe, then I am not a true Calvinist!

'If it means God loves only the elect, then I am not a true Calvinist!

'If it means I cannot and must not offer the gospel to all men, then I am not a true Calvinist!

'If it means I must take the attitude that if God wants the lost saved, he will save them without the use of means, then I am not a true Calvinist!

'If it means I cannot recognize non-Calvinists as Christians and as members of the body of Christ, nor can I fellowship with them ever at all, then I am not a true Calvinist.

'If it means I must preach on one of the five points of Calvinism each time I step into the pulpit rather than expound the Word of God verse by verse and book by book, then I am not a true Calvinist!

'If it means each time I preach I must use Calvinistic phrases and shibboleths to prove my Calvinism, then I am not a true Calvinist!

'If it means I must tear churches apart by virulent attacks on people who do not agree with me, then I am not a true Calvinist!

'If it means I must talk like a seventeenth-century Puritan, then I am not a true Calvinist!

'If it means I must become gnostic in my attitude, acting as if I and those like me are the only ones God can bless and use, then I am not a true Calvinist!'

By now his whole face was blazing, but I was not quite finished.

'But I think the truth of the matter is that I am the true Calvinist, and your brand is a distorted one which needs to be rejected and labelled as false hyper-Calvinism.'

This was the first time I had ever stood up to Jim. Previously he had made many ridiculous statements, but I had said little or nothing. Why bother to engage in worthless theological debate? Besides he had always treated me as if I were his inferior in knowledge of the Bible and doctrine. Therefore at this point my courage and bluntness of speech had not only surprised him, but left him somewhat devastated. He had probably imagined he would come in and bowl me over me with his views and his overwhelming demeanour, but I had beaten him to it.

However, I must credit him with some wisdom at this point. He obviously saw that talking with me on this subject was hopeless, so he excused himself with the parting shot that I had better stay out of the affairs of the Lime Creek Baptist Church.

I assured him that if he meant not to come to Lime Creek, not to turn up at a business meeting, or not to meet secretly with any of the people, then I would abide by his request. But if he meant not to talk to Todd, or with any of the people at all, even if they approached me, then I was convinced he had a complete misunderstanding of the term 'meddle'. In fact, according to his definition, I informed him, I was meddling with the affairs of Lime Creek simply by talking to him, because he was a member of that church.

With these words we parted company. But I knew the issue was not settled for me, for him, for Todd, or for the rest of the church. It seemed the opportunity for God to work was getting bigger, and my definition of faith told me it was not what I could do in the situation, but what God could and would do.

36.
A time of growth

The following Sunday the Lord confirmed to me something I had thought was taking place in my church, but till then I was not sure. There was definite evidence of a work of revival and renewal at the First Baptist Church. Contrary to many people's thinking, revival does not always take place during a week or two of meetings, but is a work that begins and builds up over a period of time in the life of an individual or of a church. Furthermore, it comes by the preaching of the Word of God. It is an ongoing process because attitudes and beliefs change slowly and only under the continual enlightenment and instruction of the Word of God. Men are often in a hurry and want to rush the work of God, and in that case they can do more harm to the church and souls spiritually than they do good.

Thus it was that on this Sunday I was no longer in any doubt that the Word of God which I had been preaching for these last few months was changing minds and lives. Different attitudes and ways of thinking were being manifested in all areas of the church's life. Even some formerly inactive members were beginning to return and to show an interest in the Word.

But there was another factor which helped to convince me that the Lord was beginning to revive his work. I had learned at Lime Creek that revival has two sides — an enlightening and renewal by the Word on the one hand, accompanied by a stiffening and hardening against the Word on the other. Whenever revival comes, some are renewed, but others are hardened, and even become opposed to the work God is doing — and these negative reactions are found among those who profess to be Christians.

I was now seeing this hardening in evidence at First Baptist Church, as I began to notice that some of the inactive members, and even some who attended sporadically, were showing signs of negative and belligerent attitudes. Somewhere and at some time, unless the Lord intervened, they would openly oppose the truth and the work God was doing. Strange, is it not, that when the church was lifeless, with only fifty attending, none of these people showed much if any, interest in the work of the church? But now that God was blessing, their interest revived, not to help, but to hinder.

What kind of people are those who are satisfied for a church to be dead and who do nothing to lift it from its lethargy, but yet become dissatisfied when the church begins to come alive, and then would seek to move heaven and earth to oppose it? Are these not unregenerate people?

The following Friday evening Terry and I met to conclude our study of the atonement and to introduce the next topic for our consideration.

As to the atonement, we summarized our conclusions under the following points:

1. The death of Christ had a particular design and purpose towards the elect, rather than simply a general design and purpose towards all men.

2. Since the death of Christ had a particular design and purpose (that is, to make atonement for the sins of the elect), the salvation of a people is guaranteed. A general purpose or design would only make *possible* the salvation of all men, but would *guarantee* the salvation of no one.

3, This doctrine of particular atonement is the logical result of the first two points of Calvinism. That is to say, that if man is totally depraved and cannot, and will not, come to God except on the basis of election, but God has elected a people, then the atonement is specifically designed for them in the light of God's purpose in election.

4. The Bible teaches that the death of Christ was specifically for a group, and not for all men, as can be seen in such verses as John 10:11; Ephesians 5:25-27; Matthew 1:21; Acts 20:28.

5. Christ could not have died for both the elect and the non-elect in the same sense, in view of the meaning of the atonement.

To 'atone' means that Christ satisfied all the justice and law of God; that Christ was the substitute assuming all the legal responsibilities of those for whom he died. Therefore, those for whom he satisfied completely the justice and law of God will be saved; those for whom he assumed legal responsibility will be saved; those for whom he was the substitute will be saved. If on the other hand, Christ's death was not a complete work (an atoning, substitutionary sacrifice for the legal responsibility of those he represented), then no one could be saved.

6. The verses which are often quoted as teaching a general atonement do not do so when properly and carefully interpreted.

Satisfied with our study and conclusions concerning the atonement of Christ, we turned to consider the subject of irresistible grace. I introduced the topic by referring to the notes taken in my study with Dr Sisk.

I began by stating that the doctrine of irresistible grace must be seen in its relationship to the first three points of the Calvinistic acrostic. If man is totally depraved, and therefore cannot come to God in his own strength; and if certain ones have been unconditionally chosen to be God's elect; and if the atonement of Christ is designed for these elect persons and guarantees their salvation — then it logically follows that the elect will indeed be saved. They will be irresistibly called and drawn to Christ.

I then listed several questions which arise from this doctrine:

1. What if a person wants to come to Christ for salvation, and he is not one of the elect, and therefore irresistible grace does not call him? Does that mean he cannot be saved?

2. What if one of the elect does not want to come to Christ for salvation, but irresistible grace calls him? Does that mean that God drags him over the doorstep of salvation screaming and shouting his rebellion against God?

3. What will such a doctrine do to evangelism and missions? If God is going to draw the elect irresistibly, will that not undercut the responsibility of men to repent and believe the gospel, and also the responsibility of the church to carry the gospel to all the world?

4. Doesn't such a view violate man's free agency and free will?

We also noted that some Calvinists prefer the term 'efficacious grace' to 'irresistible grace'.

We decided next time we would, first of all, seek to determine if this view was scriptural or not, and if so, how we would answer the questions I had listed.

I was so grateful that my study was not just confined to what I had learned at college, for otherwise I would never have stretched my mind to consider these truths and would have believed only what others told me was the truth.

37.
'Don't you remember me?'

I had not forgotten Todd or the Lime Creek Church, nor my conversation with Jim. I sensed a responsibility to do something, but what? I was waiting for some leading from the Lord in the matter. One possibility was that I would run into Todd at college again, and could determine his attitude in the matter, and perhaps even arrange a time to visit him. I didn't want to appear to be pressing the matter or meddling in his affairs. Finally the Lord's providence prevailed and brought us together one afternoon on the college car park following classes.

After exchanging the usual formalities, which were a little cold and strained, I made a suggestion: 'Todd, how about a coffee? Have you got time?'

His answer really hurt me, though it should not have surprised me. He said coldly, 'We've decided it might be best if I don't talk to you again in the light of your attitude towards me!'

I really knew the answer to my question before I asked it, but I wanted to make him admit it: 'Todd, who is this 'we' and 'us' you keep referring to?'

He did reply, but it was obviously a difficult answer and he looked uncomfortable: 'My assistant pastor and I feel that way.'

'Your assistant pastor?' I retorted. 'Who is that?' Again, I felt sure I knew the answer, but wanted to hear him say it.

'Jim Mitchell,' he said, hanging his head and refusing to look me in the eye.

I could have taken several lines of probing the matter, but decided to explore the subject of our friendship first: 'Todd, do you remember who you're talking to? This is Ira! Your old friend and roommate! The one who prayed for you when you were lost and struggling in sin! The one who refused to give up on you when you played religious games with God! The one who still shared a room with you when you were acting like a proper nutcase! The one who rejoiced when you were saved! The one you asked to disciple you and teach you everything God had taught him! The one who did instruct you, spending hours to establish you in the faith! The one who recommended you to Lime Creek Church! The one who still loves you and prays for you daily! The one who wants God's best for you and your life and your ministry!'

I paused, but he was still hanging his head and he said nothing, so I continued: 'And when did Jim Mitchell become your assistant pastor? The last time I heard he was only teaching a Sunday School class. Whose idea was it for him to be an assistant — surely not the church's? Don't you realize the danger of this move to make him an assistant — the danger to you and the church? When are you going to begin to think for yourself, and not be just the mouthpiece for a man who almost destroyed the church at Lime Creek once?'

He didn't answer any of my questions, but sought to shift the blame back onto me by saying, 'You're the one who taught me Calvinism, Ira. We're only carrying these doctrines to their logical conclusions.'

I'm afraid I was a little cutting and sarcastic as I replied, 'You'd better ask if you're carrying them to the *biblical* conclusions.'

When he clammed up, refusing to answer, I addressed him again, this time with great love: 'Todd, the time will come in this situation when you will need a friend and some spiritual counsel. Please call on me, no matter what time of day or night. I'll do all I can to help you when that time comes. I only pray it is not too late.'

He was suddenly very serious. 'Too late for what, Ira?'

'Too late to rescue your ministry and the Lime Creek Church, that's what!' I replied.

With these words, we parted. I was convinced that only a crisis situation, in which he came to see the truth about Jim Mitchell and his intentions, would bring him to seek my help again. Such an experience might well be the making of the preacher, though it might also break his heart. Little did I realize then that the call would come sooner than I could have expected. God's opportunity was about to become that blessing.

38.
A cry for help

I had not expected to hear from Todd soon, least of all at 1 a.m. on the Monday morning following our conversation, and after a hectic Sunday. I couldn't imagine who could be ringing (oh, what little faith I had, seeing I had told him to call me day or night!).

When I answered the jangling phone, almost knocking it to the floor in the darkness of my bedroom, I recognized Todd's voice at the other end of the line.

'Ira, this is Todd. I'm ready for that help and counsel you promised the other day. I have come to see you were right about Jim Mitchell, and I don't know what to do about it.'

I was willing to meet him anytime, anywhere, as I had promised, but I hoped it could wait until morning. We were miles apart, and as pastors, we both had to be tired from Sunday, and were in need of sleep.

But knowing he was badly hurt, and that something unusual must have taken place to trigger this call, I said, 'Todd, you name the time and the place!'

To my relief, we agreed on breakfast early the next morning, but before I let him off the phone I asked him what had happened.

'Jim told me this evening that it was God's will for me to resign as pastor of Lime Creek, and for him to be the pastor. He said he could guide and teach the church in a better and quicker way than I could. I could be his assistant, he said.'

He spoke with some fire in his voice, as if he couldn't believe the audacity of this man Jim Mitchell. I acted as if I were shocked too, but really it was completely in line with the personality of Jim

Mitchell. I didn't blame his doctrine, because he would have been that way whatever his theological position. He was a man who had to dominate, whatever place or position he took in life. The doctrine of Calvinism had not made him that way, but rather he was that way, and maybe was even a hyper-Calvinist because of it.

When we met for breakfast the next morning, the heart of our discussion centred on what Todd could do in that situation. He agreed he had created a monster and an extremely difficult problem by feeding the ego of Jim Mitchell, as he had agreed with his doctrinal extremes and allowed him to advance in authority in the church. Todd, at this point, was open and looking for answers. He would have done anything I suggested.

But that was part of the problem. Todd was a follower. When was he going to become a leader? When was he going to learn to think out these matters for himself? Would I be doing him any favours to give him a five-point plan of action? Or would I just be encouraging him to be a follower — of me again?

Therefore, I asked him bluntly what he thought he should do now in the light of this mess. The question was not just what would straighten the matter out, but what would the Lord have him do?

'Well,' he said, thinking out loud, 'I suppose the Lord would have me confess my sin.'

'What sin?' I asked, not wanting him to speak of sin in general.

'Well, I've failed and sinned as a leader. I've fallen into doctrinal error. I've had an unloving attitude towards the people. I rebelled against the counsel of the truth as you and others sought to talk to me about the matter. I've put a man in the place of God in my life, which is idolatry. And I suppose there are other areas of sin, too.'

'Wow!' I thought to myself. 'What a sensitive conscience for one who just some months ago had little evidence of any conscience at all!' Again, I saw the evidence of true regeneration in Todd's life.

'Well, what do you think you ought to do about it?' I asked.

'The first thing is to ask the Lord's forgiveness. Ira, that's what I did all last night. I hardly got any sleep. I am so sorry I have failed my Lord so miserably in these areas.'

'Then what should you do next?' I asked again, leading him one step at a time, but letting him make the decisions.

'I must apologize to the people, and I will begin tonight by asking the deacons for their forgiveness. Then Wednesday night I will ask the people to forgive me. If it is the wish of the church, I will resign and they can call another man.'

I didn't tell him, but I knew his deacons would be on his side, and would forgive and encourage him.

'What about Jim Mitchell?' I asked again.

'I guess I'll have to face him openly and bluntly in a showdown or confrontation, if necessary. I must tell him that the Lord has not led me to resign as pastor, and until he does I will remain in that position. And then I must tell him I cannot agree with his theology.'

I wanted to hear him say it, so I asked, 'You mean to say, you don't really agree with Jim's theology?'

'No, Ira, I guess I was swayed by Jim's forcefulness and overwhelming dominance. There were times when I wanted to disagree with him, or at least raise some questions, but who was I to argue with someone like Jim who's so versed in theology and doctrine? Ira, did you realize that about all he does is read theology, especially the Puritans?'

'Nothing wrong with the Puritans,' I said. 'It would do us all good to read them.'

'Well, you know what I mean, Ira. Jim has a way of out-puritanizing the Puritans sometimes. And I'll be honest with you, I don't cherish the thought of clashing with him. Why did I ever encourage him to come back to Lime Creek? Ira, would you go with me to talk to Jim?'

My heart went out to him, and I too trembled at the thought of his having to tangle with Jim in a theological discussion. But, nevertheless, I declined his invitation. I knew that it would be another instance of Todd following instead of leading and standing on his own. Even if he took a beating, it was better and indeed necessary for him to go by himself.

I did encourage him as he went to confront Jim to refuse to discuss the theological issues. I advised him to simply cover them in the blanket statement that there was too sizeable a gap in their theological understanding for them to continue working together at Lime Creek, and it would be best if Jim left.

I then asked him if Jim had any following at the church. He affirmed there were a few who had come back with him — those who had left when the church had asked him to resign — but only a few. The vast majority of the people were against Jim and his ways and his theology, and were even worried over Todd's association with him.

It seemed our discussion was just about over, when he broke down and began to cry. I wasn't prepared for this, since we had worked through the problem, with him doing the thinking and deciding. So, I asked him what was wrong.

'Well, I'm not supposed to know it, but the deacons are meeting tonight and are going to ask me to resign because of this whole mess. Ira, do you think I should resign?'

I refused to allow him to stop doing his own thinking. So, I tried to guide him, 'What do you think?'

'After praying about the matter, I think I should, if they want me to do so. But if they want me to stay, and will forgive me and work with me, I'll be glad to remain as their pastor. And I guarantee you, I'll be a much better pastor than before!'

I agreed with him, and as I did a sour thought struck my mind. Was this the old Todd I was seeing? He hadn't been willing to confess his sin or do anything to try to straighten out this mess until it appeared he was in trouble and would lose the church — his position and his pay. Was this another case I had seen so often before of repentance when he was in a tight spot? Was he really concerned with truth and righteousness, or just with the fact he could lose a church?

I didn't ask him that question, because I didn't want to hurt him still more by making him think I doubted him. But I filed it away in my mind for future reference in case he got into further difficulties after the Lord had straightened out this mess. I was really convinced that I had seen sufficient growth and Christian character since his conversion to leave little doubt that he was truly regenerate.

Later that night he rang me, rejoicing over the meeting with the deacons. They had accepted his repentance with great delight. In fact, the meeting had turned into a prayer meeting of brokenness and tears. Todd thanked me for being his friend, and he wept again over the phone. He asked me to pray for him, as he would be seeing Jim in the next few days.

I drifted off to sleep that night rejoicing too. What is it about sharing one's joy with someone else, and someone else sharing their joy with you? Isn't that an occasion for double joy? And it was a time of great joy, for deep trouble had moved past the stage of opportunity, and had wrought a deep work of growth and strengthening in God's servant.

39.
A mighty work of God

As the next week passed, I didn't think Friday evening would ever arrive. So much had happened since Terry and I had sat down to consider our theological enquiry. When that happens, you tend to forget where you are in the search. I had done some preliminary work again, but tested her jokingly to see if she had remembered.

'Do you know what our subject is?' I queried.

'Yes!' she replied confidently. 'Do you want me to lead the discussion tonight?'

It was at this point that I realized just what a unique young lady I was going to marry, as she proceeded to summarize our introduction to the subject of irresistible grace without a single note before her. As she finished, I wondered if I could have done as well without my notes!

When she had finished, we batted the summary around for a few moments, and then I led us further into the subject. First, I mentioned the last point referred to in our summary, recognizing that some Calvinists prefer the expression 'efficacious grace' to the wording of 'irresistible grace'. The term 'irresistible grace' might leave the impression that someone is forced to come to Christ and salvation against his desires, or against his will. One could almost have a picture (falsely, however) of God dragging the sinner across the threshold of salvation while he kicks and screams his rebellion, rejection and blasphemy against God for compelling him to come to salvation.

Nothing could in fact be further from the conviction of a Calvinist regarding irresistible grace! This doctrine does not mean that God forces himself on an unwilling and fighting sinner whc would rather stay in his sin, or would rather return to his sin after God saves him. Rather the doctrine asserts that though the sinner is spiritually blind, God by the Holy Spirit enables him to see the truth about himself, God and salvation. Though the sinner wants everything except God, God by the Holy Spirit grants him a desire for God and holiness. Though the sinner is powerless to break with his sin and come to God, God by the Holy Spirit enables him to turn from his sin and come to God by the gift of faith in Christ. Though the sinner is dead, God gives him new life.

Therefore there would never be a situation where one of the elect would not want to be saved, for the regenerating power of God will grant sight, desire, power and enabling to all the elect in the work of salvation. Neither would there ever be a case of someone who was not elect wanting to be saved, because if God does not move upon the heart of man, there will never be the spiritual desire, sight, power or enabling to come to Christ.

With a clear understanding of the definition of irresistible grace, and an answer to one of the most common objections to the doctrine, we turned to determine if the doctrine was found in Scripture.

First, we noted the following passages of Scripture which undeniably state that *salvation includes a regeneration, or new birth*:

'Not by works of righteousness which we have done, but according to His mercy He saved us, through the washing of regeneration and renewing of the Holy Spirit' (Titus 3:5).
'Jesus answered and said to him, "Most assuredly, I say to you, unless one is born again, he cannot see the kingdom of God"' (John 3:3).

Second, some passages may not put it in the form of regeneration or new birth, but they do show clearly that *this work of salvation is a mighty, powerful, deep work*:

'... who [God] called you out of darkness into His marvellous light' (1 Peter 2:9).
'And you He made alive, who were dead in trespasses and sins' (Ephesians 2:1).
'He who hears My word and believes in Him who sent me ... has passed from death into life' (John 5:24).

Third, some passages (including some of the ones just mentioned) show that *this work of salvation is completely the work of God and not of man,* and that it is God's prerogative and not man's:

'And what is the exceeding greatness of His power toward us who believe, according to the working of his mighty power...' (note that we believe according to the working of God's mighty power, Ephesians 1:19).

'I will give them one heart, and I will put a new spirit within them, and take the stony heart out of their flesh, and give them a heart of flesh, that they may walk in My statutes, and keep My judgements and do them; and they shall be My people, and I will be their God' (Ezekiel 11:19).

'... even so the Son gives life to whom He will' (John 5:21).

'All that the Father gives Me will come to Me; and the one who comes to Me I will by no means cast out' (John 6:37).

'No one can come to Me unless the Father who sent Me draws him; and I will raise him up at the last day' (John 6:44).

'It is the Spirit who gives life; the flesh profits nothing' (John 6:63).

'And [Jesus] said, "Therefore I have said to you that no one can come to Me unless it has been granted to him by my Father' (John 6:65).

'As You [the Father] have given Him [the Son] authority over all flesh, that He should give eternal life to as many as You [the Father] have given him [the Son]' (John 17:2).

'Now a certain woman named Lydia heard us. She was a seller of purple from the city of Thyatira, who worshipped God. The Lord opened her heart to heed the things spoken by Paul' (Acts 16:14).

'And as many as had been appointed to eternal life believed' (Acts 13:48).

'Of His own will He brought us forth by the word of truth...' (James 1:18)

Therefore we came to the following conclusions:

1. *Salvation is a deep work, requiring great power to effect it*

It is pictured as a resurrection from death to life.
It is also pictured as moving from darkness to light.
It is a new birth or regeneration.

2. Salvation is such a deep work that it can only be accomplished by the power of God

Regeneration is by the power of the Holy Spirit.
Faith is by his power.
Newness of life is given by his power.
The Spirit makes alive, while the flesh profits nothing.
The Lord must open the heart by his power.

3. Salvation, as a deep work of God, is given according to God's will

Only those given to the Son by the Father come to Christ.
Eternal life is given only to those given to the Son by the Father.
The Son gives life to whom he wills.
No one comes unless the Father draws him.
The Lord must open the heart.
Those believe who have been appointed to eternal life.

With these clear premises from the Word of God, we agreed that we could not disagree with the doctrine of irresistible grace. Further, we noted its consistency with the first three points of Calvinism. Since man is totally depraved and cannot come to God in his own strength, nor does he possess any desire to come to God; and since God has chosen to save a people and that choice is based on his own will; and since Christ died as the full payment of the sin of this chosen people; then it is also true that God will save this people, irresistibly calling and regenerating them by his power.

That left us one more area of study — the doctrine of the perseverance of the saints. But I didn't know when we would get round to it , especially since we had planned a wedding during the Christmas season, which was now only a few weeks away! We spent the rest of the evening discussing the intricacies of the wedding plans — not nearly as interesting (at least to me) as discussing theology!

40.
A question of persevering

I didn't hear from Todd again concerning his meeting with Jim Mitchell until the next Monday when I ran into him at college. As he told me about their confrontation, I felt almost as if I had been present. Good old spineless Todd had finally stood up for the truth with backbone and conviction.

He said he had called Jim into his office on Sunday, and had suggested that he and his family move on to another church. Evidently this caught Jim completely by surprise, since he had hoped to be the pastor of the church again soon. When Jim asked Todd why he thought he should leave, Todd replied that their theologies were too different, and that Jim's ambition to lead the church again was not in God's will. Todd told him he would be welcome to stay if he could submit to the church's leadership, but Jim had not shown any evidence of being able to do so in the past.

Jim's response ran the whole gamut from doctrinal argumentation, through lambasting Todd's abilities as pastor and castigating me for 'having got at Todd', to threatening to take some people with him when he left. But Todd played it cool by refusing to argue theology with him, or to be intimidated by his threats, and by informing him that the deacons and church stood with their pastor, and that the only people who would leave with him would be the ones who had left before.

I was impressed by Todd's attitude as he told me about this incident. It wasn't the proud spirit of someone who had bested another in battle (a spirit the old Todd would have manifested), but it was the humble attitude of one who had sought to follow his Lord in doing his will in a very tough situation. I saw that not only had a very serious issue been settled at Lime Creek, but also that a man of God had emerged from the battle.

Our conversation closed with Todd asking if I would help him settle the theological questions Jim had raised. I replied that I would, but we must do it in one meeting, and he must do the homework and share his findings with me. I would not disciple him any longer. Besides, I had a church to pastor, and a wedding coming up soon. We set a date in early December when we would meet for discussion.

The next Friday evening Terry and I met for our consideration of the fifth and final point of Calvinism. We began by the usual review of the doctrine.

1. The doctrine of perseverance is the logical conclusion of the other previous four points of the Calvinist acrostic

If man is totally depraved, and cannot do anything to help himself spiritually; and if God is absolutely sovereign in the matter of election, choosing the elect on the basis of his will, and his will alone; and if Christ's death was for the elect, guaranteeing their salvation; and if God calls the elect irresistibly, then it follows that God will assure the final salvation of the elect — that is, they will persevere to the final end.

If the elect did not persevere, then the eternal election of God would fail, and this the Calvinist could not admit. If God decrees something, it will certainly come to pass, including the final salvation of the elect.

If the elect did not persevere, then the death of Christ would be a failure, because its design was to guarantee the salvation of the elect.

If the elect did not persevere, then the grace of God could be resisted by the saved (they could reject it in a final manner after they are saved), even though grace was irresistible before they were saved!

2. Definition of the doctrine

The doctrine of perseverance says that those who are the elect, because they have been the object of God's eternal decree of election and because they have been the object of Christ's atonement, will continue in the way of salvation, as the same power of God that saved them will also keep and sanctify them unto their final salvation.

3. The doctrine of perseverance does not rule out backsliding by a believer

However, it does rule out the possibility that someone can profess to be a Christian and yet live in a supposedly backslidden state for a number of years without facing the chastening hand of God.

Backsliding will occur among Christians, but the doctrine of perseverance says that the true believer will not remain in that state endlessly. If a person does, he had better put a big question mark beside his profession of faith.

4. The doctrine of perseverance does not include the concept of a 'carnal Christian'

A carnal Christian, as defined by some, is someone who has been truly saved, yet lives as if he is lost. He has made a profession of faith, and may have lived like a Christian for a while, but now he has gone back to the world, and both those around him in the world and those in the church wouldn't be able to tell he was a Christian. Only God knows his heart. He may spend the rest of his life in this condition, but because of his salvation experience, he will be in eternity with Christ. He is carnal, but he is a Christian. Or he is a Christian, but he is carnal. The Calvinist would say, if there is no perseverance, there is no salvation; and if there is salvation, there will be perseverance.

5. The security of the believer is only half the doctrine

The doctrine of perseverance includes the security of the believer, but security by itself is only half the doctrine and leaves false thinking and living in its wake

The Baptist concept of 'Once saved, always saved,' is only half the coin, and with only half the coin it can become a dangerous doctrine.

The doctrine of perseverance, according to the Calvinist, has two sides — security and perseverance. Yet one cannot exist without the other. The Baptist doctrine of eternal security ('Once saved, always saved') overlooks or neglects the necessity of perseverance as the proof of true salvation. Thus by telling a person of eternal security without telling him of the reality of perseverance as the proof of salvation, one could produce the same results as the 'carnal Christian' doctrine — people who think they are saved but who are not. The doctrine of eternal security without the other side of the coin becomes a licence to sin for those who have merely professed faith in Christ, but who have never truly been saved.

The Calvinist doctrine of perseverance gives both comfort to the believer (he is eternally secure) and reality to his profession (he realizes the proof of his salvation is a perseverance in the Christian life).

I didn't realize this summary would take us so long to formulate and discuss. We decided we would have to wait till another time to test whether it was scriptural. The next hour or so went much more slowly for me as we discussed matters pertaining to the wedding. I was discovering early in the ministry that weddings would not be the part of my work that thrilled me the most. I was eager enough about getting married, but I had never realized that there were so many details. We had finished the planning of the service long ago. Now it was the other things, which women seem to enjoy more than men, that had to be discussed.

I tried to look as interested and as happy as possible, as we discussed these matters which Terry brought up, but at times she realized my heart was elsewhere. But she didn't seem to mind too much and she didn't scold me about it, which I appreciated. Maybe if we had been studying the theology of marriage, I would have been more excited. As we sometimes have to in the Christian life, I was persevering in a situation that was not much to my liking!

41.
The proof of salvation

What with church responsibilities, including several funerals, and end-of-term college work, it was not until the Thanksgiving break, in fact on Thanksgiving Day, that Terry and I finally sat down in the afternoon to discuss further the matter of the perseverance of the saints.

After reviewing the doctrine as we had discussed it previously, we plunged into the question of whether it was scriptural. We noted several classes of Scripture passages helpful to our thinking.

The security of the believer

First, there were many passages which clearly taught that the believer could not lose his salvation, including the following:

'Who shall separate us from the love of Christ? Shall tribulation, or distress, or persecution, or famine, or nakedness, or peril, or sword? As it is written: "For Your sake we are killed all day long; we are accounted as sheep for the slaughter." Yet in all these things we are more than conquerors through Him who loved us. For I am persuaded that neither death nor life, nor angels nor principalities nor powers, nor things present nor things to come, nor height, nor depth, nor any other created thing, shall be able to separate us from the love of God which is in Christ Jesus our Lord' (Romans 8:35-39).

'All that the Father gives Me will come to Me, and the one who comes to Me I will by no means cast out' (John 6:37).

'My sheep hear My voice, and I know them, and they follow Me. And I give them eternal life, and they shall never perish; neither shall anyone snatch them out of My hand. My Father, who has given them to me, is greater than all; and no one is able to snatch them out of My Father's hand' (John 10:27-29)

'Being confident of this very thing, that He who has begun a good work in you will complete it until the day of Jesus Christ' (Philippians 1:6).

'For the gifts and the calling of God are irrevocable' (Romans 11:29).

'For I know whom I have believed and am persuaded that He is able to keep what I have committed to Him until that Day' (2 Timothy 1:12).

'For by one offering He has perfected for ever those who are being sanctified' (Hebrews 10:14).

Even the expression 'eternal' or 'everlasting life' surely speaks of a salvation which, by its very nature, never would, or never could end.

'Most assuredly, I say to you, he who believes in me has everlasting life' (John 6:47).

'Most assuredly, I say to you, he who hears My word and believes in him who sent me has everlasting life, and shall not come into judgement, but has passed from death into life' (John 5:24).

Surely both these verses speak clearly of a life that will never end?

The perseverance of the believer

On the other side of the coin of the truth of the believer's eternal security, we noted passages which spoke of perseverance — that is, that the true believer will continue in the faith, and not turn from it back into a life of sin.

Matthew 7:13-14. We began with Matthew 7:13-14, which reads, 'Enter by the narrow gate; for wide is the gate and broad is the way that leads to destruction, and there are many who go in by it

Because narrow is the gate and difficult is the way which leads to
life, and there are few who find it .'

From this passage we noted that the wide gate leads to the broad
way and the narrow gate leads to the narrow way. There is no such
possibility as walking through the narrow gate and ending up on the
broad road, nor can one pass through the broad gate and end up on
the narrow way. If someone is walking on the broad road, he has not
passed through the narrow gate, and if someone is walking on the
narrow road, he did not reach it by the broad gate. And surely our
Lord's words, 'There are few who find it,' should be a warning and
admonition to us that we need to be sure that we are truly saved. Does
this passage not indicate that there are many walking the broad road
who think they have passed through the narrow gate, but are actually
mistaken?

Matthew 7:16-18. Then we turned to Matthew 7:16-18: 'Youwill
know them by their fruits. Do men gather grapes from thornbushes
or figs from thistles? Even so, every good tree bears good fruit, but
a bad tree bears bad fruit. A good tree cannot bear bad fruit, nor can
a bad tree bear good fruit.'

I asked Terry what the context was here. After browsing quickly
through the surrounding text, she replied that these words are
spoken primarily with reference to false prophets.

I agreed but added, 'Yet are there not principles laid down here
which apply to every professing believer?' Without waiting for an
answer, I suggested the following principles:

1. The fruit (the way a person conducts his or her life) tells you
something about a person.
2. A saved person will bear good fruit (good conduct of life).
3. A saved person's conduct will not be consistently evil.
4. lost person will not bear good fruit (the proper conduct of
life).

In other words, we can know someone has received the new birth
by the character and trend of his or her life. The saved person will
be characterized by a holy life, and it cannot be constantly and
consistently tending towards a life of evil. The unconverted person
will also have a character and trend of life that is telling, and it cannot
be truly a consistently holy and good life.

Therefore, for anyone to claim to be saved and then to live a constantly and continually unholy life proves that his or her profession is not genuine. The truly saved person will persevere in holiness and godliness over a period of time.

Matthew 7:21-23. The next passage we considered was Matthew 7:21-23: 'Not everyone who says to Me, "Lord, Lord," shall enter the kingdom of heaven, but he who does the will of My Father in heaven. Many will say to Me in that day, "Lord, Lord, have we not prophesied in Your name, cast out demons in Your name, and done many wonders in your name?" And then I will declare to them, "I never knew you; depart from me, you who practise lawlessness."'

As we discussed this verse we concluded that Christ is stating that the real test of salvation is not simply a profession of faith in Christ (these people called him 'Lord'), nor is it the presence of certain works (preaching or even miracles). Rather, the real test of salvation is doing the will of the Father. It is not that doing the will of the Father saves a person, but that the saved person will do the will of the Father. He or she will persevere!

Matthew 13:5-6. We then read Matthew 13:5-6: 'Some fell upon stony places, where they had not much earth; and they immediately sprang up because they had no depth of earth. But when the sun was up, they were scorched, and because they had no root they withered away.'

In handling this passage we recalled its context — the parable of the sower. As the sower did his work, the seed fell on different kinds of soil. Some fell on stony ground, and soon the sprouts began to spring up with every evidence that they were real and lasting. But when the sun came out, these on the stony ground soon withered and died, because they had no deep roots.

We concluded that this passage indicated that persons may respond with a gladness and apparent correctness to the gospel message. They may even appear to give evidence of a true conversion experience. But when the trials and persecutions of the Christian life come, they fall by the wayside because they were never truly saved. They do not persevere, and that is a sign they were not saved.

At this point, Terry remarked, 'That really is frightening, you know!'

I thought I knew what she meant, but asked none the less, 'What do you mean?'

'Well,' she began, 'that means that many of those on our church rolls, that we normally call Christians because at one point in their lives they made a profession of faith, may not really be saved!'

I smiled, and she must have thought I was laughing at her because she continued: 'Seriously, how many of those making professions of faith today in our churches really persevere? How many make a profession of faith, and take off like a house on fire in the supposed living of the Christian life, only to fall by the wayside within a matter of a few weeks or months? And yet we still carry them on the church rolls, and consider them to be Christians, and even tell them they are eternally secure and will never lose their salvation, when Jesus, according to this parable, said they never were saved at all!'

I rejoiced in my heart to see how she had grasped the real meaning and application of the passage for our day. She had expressed my convictions exactly! Perseverance is the proof of salvation.

Matthew 24:13. Finally, we turned to Matthew 24:13: 'And because lawlessness will abound, the love of many will grow cold. But he who endures to the end shall be saved.

Having done a little study on this passage, I noted for Terry's benefit the background of this verse. It is in a context having to do with the end times and some people seem to want to confine the principle it contains (endurance to the end as the sign of true salvation) to the final days of the age, and not to our day and times.

We agreed that the principle stated here is clear — that the evidence of true salvation is continuance to the end. It does not teach that someone is saved *by enduring to the end*, but that if a person is saved, he or she *will endure to the end*. On the other hand, failure to persevere or endure to the end is a sign that someone does not possess true salvation.

We also agreed that this principle was not just for one age — the last days. Could it possibly be that during the end time, when persecution was particularly fierce, that the Lord would demand perseverance as the evidence of salvation, while in days prior to that period he would be lenient and lax, allowing his own to walk loosely in sin? Even more serious, could it be that salvation in the final days would be more powerful and life-changing than in the days prior to that time? Would not salvation be the same in both periods of the history of the church?

About this time a knock came at the front door of Terry's house where we were meeting. On hearing it I uttered my usual query when facing an unexpected and unwanted interruption: 'Who can that possibly be?'

I was rather startled when Todd and a young lady walked into the room as Terry opened the door. I was even more startled when he introduced his companion as his fiancée! Evidently, he had just proposed marriage to her, and they were so overjoyed that they had to tell someone — and they chose us! I guess I should have been flattered to be chosen to share their joy, but I couldn't help but be a little sceptical, asking myself if this wasn't a little premature for Todd, in the light of his past history of a long string of broken romantic relationships.

We congratulated them, but I knew some time in the near future I had to ask Todd some serious questions about his most recent engagement. Perhaps I could do it when we talked about his questions on theology.

42.
The end of the search

With our wedding fast approaching (we were getting married during the Christmas season), we found little time for our theological study. I was amazed that time could go so fast, and yet drag so slowly at the same time. It was moving too quickly to do everything we needed to get done, but yet too slowly to suit us as far as our forthcoming marriage was concerned. But we were determined to get the theological study finished before the day of the wedding!

Therefore, on the second Friday evening of December, we made time to consider the second part of the doctrine of perseverance. We had concluded that the Bible teaches the security of the believer — no question about that. But we had also looked at several verses which convinced us that security is only one part of the blessed truth of the fifth point of Calvinism. The other side of the coin is the matter of perseverance. We had considered several passages, notably Matthew 7:13-14,16-18; 13:5-6; 24:13, and had concluded that they all taught the doctrine of perseverance. Now we turned briefly to some other key verses of the New Testament.

2 Corinthians 5:17. As we began, I asked Terry to read 2 Corinthians 5:17 for us, and she responded: 'Therefore, if anyone is in Christ, he is a new creation; old things have passed away; behold, all things have become new.'

We concluded, as we discussed this verse, that it teaches that when someone is in Christ, he has experienced a great change and transformation of life and character. He is in a different state. He has new views of himself, of his own nature, of his life, of God, of his sins, of the world, of the devil, of the truth and of his purpose and goal in life. He has new affections, a new mind, new desires, new aims, new enjoyments, new habits, new hopes — in fact, a new life.

I remarked, 'This passage declares, among other truths, what salvation is not!'

'That's right,' Terry chimed in strongly at this point. 'Salvation is more than a profession of faith, or a dip in a baptistry, or leading a moral life, or conformity to external rules of religion. It is more than covering up the old corrupt nature by culture and education. It is more than an emotional experience, pious feelings and thoughts about God. It is more than working in a church for a few years; more than knowing the truths and doctrines of the Bible. Salvation, according to this verse, is the supernatural transformation in which a person is both renewed inwardly and transformed outwardly. The person experiencing salvation is a new creation — old things have passed away, and all things are new.'

And then she added the clincher: 'I wonder why our churches only preach and apply the positive aspect of this verse — that to be saved is to be a new creation. Yet they never press the negative implication or truth found here — that to fail to give evidence of being a new creation is to be lost!'

I answered by playing devil's advocate: 'Judge not, that you be not judged!' This was a warning I had heard quoted many times as I had discussed these issues with fellow students, pastors and even church members.

But again Terry amazed me by proving she had been studying the Word on her own as she shot back, 'Jesus said in John 7:24, "Do not judge according to appearance, but judge with righteous judgement."'

I knew the verse, and in fact I had used it myself several times in discussions, but I was astounded that she knew it. So I asked, 'How do you know that verse?'

She didn't raise her eyebrows in answering, but her reply cut me down to size, as she said, 'You're not the only one discussing theology out there day by day and week by week with other people!'

With that we moved to the book of Hebrews.

Hebrews 3:6, 14. I read the verses for us this time: 'But Christ as a Son over His own house, whose house we are if we hold fast the confidence and the rejoicing of the hope firm to the end... For we have become partakers of Christ if we hold the beginning of our confidence steadfast to the end'(Hebrews 3:6,14).

We recognized that some people might like to use these verses to prove salvation by works, saying that both verses declare that we are part of Christ's house and are partakers of his salvation, if we hold our confidence steadfast to the end. They would see salvation as being the result of our faithfulness and steadfastness. But such an interpretation puts the cart before the horse. It is not that these verses teach that salvation is the result of our faithfulness and steadfastness, but our faithfulness and steadfastness are the result of our salvation.

I tried to illustrate this point by saying, 'Suppose I had in my hand what appeared to be a small piece of glass, and I were to say, "This is a diamond — if it will cut the glass in the window-pane across the room." Then suppose I crossed the room to the window, and used the object in my hand to cut the window-pane. Did the object I held in my hand become a diamond because it cut the window, or did the fact that it cut the window prove that it already was a diamond?'

Similarly, perseverance does not make a person a Christian, but it proves that person really is a Christian. And these verses in Hebrews do not teach that salvation is the result of our faithfulness and steadfastness, but our faithfulness and steadfastness are produced as a result of our salvation.

Revelation 2-3. Finally, we turned to the book of Revelation. We didn't take a lot of time to discuss these passages in detail, but we noted the emphasis on overcoming in the second and third chapters. There we read,

> 'To him who overcomes...
>> 'I will give to eat from the tree of life, which is in the midst of the Paradise of God' (2:7).
>> '... I will give some of the hidden manna to eat. And I will give him a white stone, and on the stone a new name written which no one knows except him who receives it' (2:17).
>> 'I will grant to sit with Me on My throne, as I also overcame and sat down with My Father on His throne' (3:21).

'He who overcomes...
  'shall not be hurt by the second death' (2:11).
  'shall be clothed in white garments' (3:5).
  'I will make him a pillar in the temple of My God, and he
    shall go out no more. And I will write on him the name
    of My God and the name of the city of My God, the
    New Jerusalem, which comes down out of heaven
    from my God. And I will write on him My new name'
    (3:12).

'He who overcomes, and keeps my works until the end,
  to him I will give power over the nations' (2:26).

We spent our remaining time asking why the churches of today
still emphasize eternal security, but no longer teach or apply the
doctrine of perseverance. We asked the following questions: Could
it be that a faulty evangelism (faulty because of faulty doctrine),
which has been producing defective fruit, must have a weak and
faulty doctrine of perseverance? That is to say, could it be that, since
we have a shallow concept of salvation, and since we rush people
quickly and eagerly into a profession of faith, not instructing them
in the essentials of true salvation, that we need to convince them as
well as ourselves that they are truly saved, even if they fall by the
wayside and do not persevere?

If we understood salvation correctly, including perseverance,
wouldn't we in the churches have to change our evangelistic
practices, and also be forced to face these people with the fact that
there was no evidence they were truly saved? And wouldn't this be
difficult, since many of them were our dearest friends and closest
relatives — people we had assured they possessed eternal salvation
on the grounds of a false understanding of eternal security? Could
we ever bring ourselves to admit our faulty doctrine and our false
evangelistic practices? Harder still, could we ever come to admit
that our dear friends and loved ones have not escaped the wrath to
come, but have only made a profession of faith which is worthless
without perseverance?

We came sadly to the conclusion that the doctrine of biblical
perseverance has been scrapped and the doctrine of eternal security
(which is only one side of the truth) has been magnified to cover our
faulty doctrine and our false converts, and to soothe our consciences

concerning our false fruit, especially our friends and loved ones who fail to show the true evidence of salvation, that is, perseverance.

'This is the problem with the church where I am pastor, and in almost every other church of our denomination!' I thought to myself, as Terry went to answer the phone. 'We have poured lost people into the church and we have convinced ourselves that they are saved, and have even allowed them to think they are saved as well, even though they give no evidence of perseverance. We label them as "backslidden" or as "carnal Christians", and hope they will "come back" to the Lord or eventually "grow in grace". All the time during that period we recognize them as saved people, keep them as members of the church, and give them a voice in the decisions of the church though they give no evidence of spiritual-mindedness or spiritual concern, let alone of salvation. The only time they come to church is during some special service, including a special business meeting to fight against the pastor or the spiritual people of the church. And to this kind of meeting they come in abundance when stirred up by others in the same condition.'

I shuddered as I thought, not only of the hundreds of such persons who still were members of the church I pastored, but of the damage they were doing against the testimony of the church, and of the damage they could do in any business meeting they chose to attend.

I wanted to pray, but I didn't even know how to pray — the problem was so massive and seemingly impossible. All I could say was, 'Help, Lord! It's beyond me to solve this problem even in my own church!'

In my heart I knew I would have to face it again some day, as I had when I had tried to move into the manse.

When Terry came back from the phone, I shared my burden with her, and we prayed together about it.

Then, knowing we had finally come to the end of our search, I asked her, 'Young lady, are you a Calvinist?'

I smiled as she replied, not even hesitating, 'Yes, sir — without question! Are you?'

I nodded in firm agreement, and then muttered jokingly, 'Well, I guess I can go ahead and marry you now — we're in doctrinal agreement!'

But all that remark got me was a cushion in my face.

43.
Questions for the preacher

The weeks of December preceding the marriage were passing quickly, when Todd and I finally got together to discuss the questions he had raised earlier in one of our discussions. We met at my office one Saturday morning.

I had asked him to draw up in advance the questions he wanted to discuss, so we could spend our limited amount of time effectually. He impressed me with his organization as he handed me a sheet of items for us to consider. In the past he would have come without one single note and would have expected me to start the ball rolling.

His single sheet of paper listed the following questions:

1. Does God love the non-elect?
2. Can we challenge all men to come to Christ in faith and repentance, since many of them are not the elect?
3. Should we offer the gospel to all men, or just to the elect only?
4. Can a Calvinist practise evangelism?
5. Can a Calvinist engage in missions?
6. Should a Calvinist use means in doing the Lord's work?
7. Should a Calvinist expound one of the five points of Calvinism each time he gets in the pulpit?

Realizing we had just this Saturday morning, and not wishing to prolong the discussion, I told Todd I would give him some short general answers, with suggestions as to where to find further ideas on the subjects raised. I added this meant I would do most of the talking. That was fine by him. If he needed to discuss them again after further study on his part, we agreed we could get together some time in the new year — after the wedding and Christmas.

Does God love the non-elect?

I began by pointing out to Todd the grounds some might find for denying God's love for those who were not elect. I quoted Malachi 1:2-3, where it says God loved Jacob and hated Esau. I also referred to Paul's quotation of this passage in Romans 9:13, where God says, 'Jacob I have loved, but Esau I have hated.'

I added that some might use the Scripture passage that says that the one who does not believe in Jesus Christ has the wrath of God abiding on him. Wouldn't that mean that God does not love such a person?

I decided to deal with the verses in their reverse order.

I began by asking, 'What is the basis for denying God's love to the non-elect? Is it that people believe that the one who is under the wrath of God cannot at the same time be the recipient of the love of God ?'

Ephesians 2:3. I didn't wait for his answer, but referring to Ephesians 2:3, I pointed out, 'Doesn't the Bible say that we were *all* at one time the children of wrath? Then doesn't that mean that one who is under the wrath of God can be loved by God at the same time? Otherwise there would be no possibility of God loving the elect, because they were also at one time under the wrath of God according to that verse.'

He nodded in agreement, so I continued, 'All men are under God's wrath, according to Ephesians 2:3. But we know also that God has loved the elect, as seen in his granting them a gracious salvation based on his sovereign grace and love. Therefore God has loved, and does love, some who are under his wrath. But does he love all men who are under his wrath? Does he love the non-elect? Doesn't the fact that they are still under his wrath, and that they will always be under his wrath, show that he does not love them?'

Matthew 5: 44. To answer that question, I suggested we turn to Matthew 5:44 and that he read it for us, which he did. I suggested he note as he read that Jesus was speaking: 'But I say to you, love your enemies, bless those who curse you, do good to those who hate you, and pray for those who spitefully use you and persecute you.'

The light dawned in his mind and he blurted out, 'Oh, I get it! Since Jesus commanded us to love our enemies, it is clear that he also loved his enemies, and that the Father loves the enemies of the truth also. There could hardly be a command from God for us to love our enemies, if God did not love his enemies as well.'

I added by way of further clarification, 'And this is the *agape* kind of love — the divine kind of love, of which man is not capable. Which is to say that man is not able to love in this manner (love his enemies) except by God's power of love.'

Todd picked up the line of thought again as he thought out loud: 'And that means that if we love men in this manner only as God enables us, then it is God loving these kind of people (our enemies) through us. And considering that these are our enemies because they are God's enemies first (they hate us because of our relationship to him), then it is a case of God loving his enemies — even the non-elect.

Mark 10:21. Next I suggested that we turn to Mark 10:21 and that he read it for us as well. After eagerly finding the passage, he read, 'Then Jesus, looking at him, loved him, and said to him, "One thing you lack: Go your way, sell whatever you have and give to the poor, and you will have treasure in heaven; and, come, take up the cross, and follow Me." But he was sad at this word, and went away grieved, for he had great posesssions.'

I then commented: 'Here we have the story of the rich young ruler who came to Christ, and yet would not surrender his life to hm. As far as we know, he was not one of the elect, and yet the text says that Christ loved him.'

At this point I noticed how quickly the time was passing, and wondered if we were spending too much time on one question. I suggested that Todd study the matter further on his own, and that we move to the next problem.

Can we challenge all men to come to Christ?

We didn't have time to go into the reasons why some argue that we cannot challenge all men to come to Christ. Rather, I decided to go directly to the heart of the answer — did Christ and the apostles challenge the non-elect with their responsibility to repent and come to Christ?

I pointed out that the message of John the Baptist was one of repentance (Matthew 3:2), and the context seems to indicate that the message was presented to all who were present, even Pharisees and Sadducees.

Again, in the preaching of Christ, there is no indication that his command to men to repent and believe was limited to just the elect (see, for example, Matthew 4:17; 11:20; 12:41; Luke 13:3).

Again the message of the disciples and apostles was a call to all to repent (see Mark 16:12; Acts 17:30). And didn't Peter's sermon on the Day of Pentecost go out to all men who were present that day?

We concluded that there is not to be found in the Bible any limitation concerning the proclamation of the gospel message. It is to go out to all men. Even the Great Commission challenges the church to take the gospel to every creature (Mark 16:15), while Paul himself states that the gospel was preached to every creature (Colossians 1:23).

In view of the time, I pointed out that these facts we had just mentioned actually answered several of the questions on his sheet.

1. Can we challenge all men to come to Christ in faith and repentance, since many of them are not the elect? Yes, we must! It was the practice of Christ and the apostles.

2. Should we offer the gospel to all men, or just to the elect only? We must offer the gospel to all men. It was the practice of Christ and the apostles.

3. Can a Calvinist practise evangelism? Definitely. He not only can, but he must! It is commanded in the Great Commission. He does so trusting God to accomplish his will and purpose.

4. Can a Calvinist engage in missions? Yes, he must. This too is commanded in the Great Commission. This work too is done trusting God for his will and purpose to be accomplished.

I wished I could have had more time to consider these questions, but I could only pray and trust that the Holy Spirit would guide Todd further in developing the answers more deeply. We were now left with two remaining questions.

Should a Calvinist use means in doing the Lord's work?

Obviously this concern centred on the question: 'If the end is predestined, why should man concern himself with the means which lead to the end?' Or, to put it more specifically concerning election, 'If some are elect, will they not be saved regardless of the means or events which precede or accompany their salvation?' Or, in regards to the perseverance of the believer, the question is, 'If the elect are guaranteed perseverance, does there need to be concern for means between their salvation and their final consummation?'

I began by stating the principle: 'The answer to these questions must not be sought in human reason, but as always from the Word of God.' But then I acknowledged we might wonder where the Word of God could possibly speak on this issue.

I reminded Todd of Christ's statement that none of his disciples should ever perish (John 10:27-29). Yet Christ himself in John 17:11 prays for the keeping of these disciples. Obviously, therefore, God's predestination ('They shall never perish') does not render void the use of means (Christ praying for his disciples).

Further, I suggested that we consider the book of Hebrews, especially the warning chapters, such as chapter 10. Why give these warnings if God has decreed his people shall be conformed to the image of Christ in all holiness? Don't these passages teach that God himself has established a clear connection between his predestined ends and the means by which they are reached?

Should a Calvinist expound one of the five points each time he preaches?

This last question was in some ways the easiest of the lot to answer. The Scriptures command the preacher to 'preach the word' (2 Timothy 4:2). The command is not to preach 'the five points of Calvinism', or even to 'preach doctrine'! Obviously, in the preaching of the Word (an expository setting forth of the Word of God, book by book or subject by subject) there will be the preaching of doctrine and the five points of Calvinism will be covered. But that is a far cry from feeling you must preach one of the five points every time you get into the pulpit.

This is not to say, a series on the five points of Calvinism is never in order. There would be value in presenting such a series as the Lord might lead. But again, that is not the same as preaching on the five points in every sermon.

As I finished these remarks, Todd began to gather up his notes and his Bible. We both knew our time was up. He thanked me for helping him in these matters. I told him it had been my joy and privilege, but there was one other matter that concerned me in his life more than these doctrinal matters.

He hung his head, as if he expected and knew what I was about to say.

So I spoke in a straightforward manner: 'Todd, I hope you really do know it is God's will for you to marry this young lady to whom you are engaged!'

I continued, 'I would not attempt, nor do I have any desire to play the Holy Spirit in your life, but I would urge you to keep the matter constantly before him with an open mind concerning his leading — even that it might mean ending the relationship.'

His last words remained with me: 'Well, Ira, if I make a mistake in this matter, I will be the one who will have to pay for it.'

I could not let him leave without one more word on the subject, as I boldy but truthfully chided him: 'But Todd, I'm not sure you realize what a great price you will have to pay for your mistake!'

44.
An end and a beginning

The search was now over! We had come to an understanding of the doctrines of grace — those doctrines known so often as Calvinism. We had sought to weigh them against Scripture. And now we both agreed that these doctrines, when properly understood (not as characterized by some) had not only been the historical position of Baptists, but they were also scriptural. In our last session together we took note of the differences these doctrines would make in our lives practically for the ministry.

Methods of evangelism

Firstly, we saw that the doctrines of Calvinism will affect the methods of evangelism used by a church.

The fear that Calvinism will destroy evangelism is unfounded, for some of the greatest preachers and evangelists of history have been Calvinists. But on the other hand, Calvinism will influence the methods and practices of evangelism. It is certainly not sensible or scriptural to do the work of evangelism using any method, just for the sake of being able to say that we are practising evangelism. Our evangelistic practices must be consistent with Scripture and its theology. Evangelism must be done in God's way and by God's power, otherwise we might create a monstrous system of methods and means which produce decisions but not the true fruit of the Holy Spirit.

The Calvinist realizes that he does not have the power within himself to convert people to Christ, but that the power of God is working within him to call forth the elect. It is our responsibility to preach the gospel to every creature throughout the world, and trust the Holy Spirit to do his work of calling out the people of God.

Better preachers of the Word of God

Secondly, the doctrines of Calvinism should make men better preachers of the Word of God.

Knowing that it is not in us, nor is it even our responsibility to convert men and women, and knowing that God does his work through the preaching of the Word of God, we will be moved more and more away from the methods of the flesh to the solid preaching of the Word of God. The result of this preaching of the Word will be truer and more stable converts.

It had become our conviction that many pastors in our land preach very little of the Word of God, even though some of them might pride themselves on their conservative outlook. They do not take a text, a passage, or a theme, and study exegetically the verses involved, and then build a solid biblical sermon from these labours. Instead they preach their experiences, or someone else's stories or experiences. The main part of their sermon is taken up, not with the meat of the Word, but with stories and illustrations, with possibly a verse read at the beginning and a few others thrown in along the way.

A man should not think he has preached the Word just because he has stirred excitement, or given out some information, or read a text in the pulpit, or got a few people to make decisions, or talked about God, Christ or the Bible, or occupied a pulpit for a certain length of time, or become emotional while in the pulpit. A person can do all these things and never preach the Word of God.

To preach the Word is to study the Bible in depth, including its grammar, the word meanings, the context, the parallel passages, and then to build a sermon from that labour and study. Obviously, to preach the Word you must spend time delving into the Word. The man who rests in the doctrines of Calvinism will do that work joyously, not fretting over whether or not he gets decisions. He knows it is his responsibility to enter the pulpit saturating his mind with the Word of God, and to preach it trusting God through the Word to convict and save sinners.

On the other hand, if we feel it is our duty and responsibility to move upon men's wills in order to cause them to make a decision, we will become exciters and exhorters, open to the possibility of attracting every foul and offensive method (foul and offensive, that is, to God though it might be pleasing and alluring to men) for evangelism, worship and preaching. Such techniques may produce the desired decisions, but not stable spiritual fruit. This is not to say that the Calvinist preaches without compassion and urgency. But it is to say he preaches the Word of God in urgency and power and trusts God to do the work.

Methods of receiving people into the church

The doctrines of Calvinism will strongly influence our methods of receiving new members into the local church, thus purifying the church and saving it from becoming a mixed multitude.

The Baptist who is a Calvinist realizes that only the elect and those who are truly born again are fit candidates for membership into the local church. Such convictions will have practical results in the ministry:

1. He will receive new members into the church joyously, but not with overzealous blindness, simply because someone has made a profession of faith. Knowing that Satan is always busy seeking to counterfeit, or falsify, the work of God, he will be careful to warn those desiring baptism and membership of the possibility of a false profession.

2. He will challenge them with the necessity to count the cost of becoming a Christian and following Christ.

3. He will face them with the responsibility which will be theirs as members of the church.

4. He will inform them of the importance of the church watching over their souls with a tender and loving care after they have been received into membership, even to the necessity of admonition and discipline should they become unfaithful or lax in the duties of the Christian life.

5. He will tell them they are uniting with a fellowship of God's people, and that such a union requires a withdrawal from extreme individualistic tendencies in order to enter into the sacrificial commitment of their persons to that fellowship.

6 He will require lovingly of them, even before receiving them into the membership of the church, some evidence of a true conversion experience and regeneration.

182

A journey in grace

7. He will share with them the standards, doctrines, dutiesand obligations of church membership, expressing also what they can expect in return from the church in relation to their lives, family and spiritual growth.

Surely these practices, had Baptists been faithful to them through the years, would have spared us the mixed multitude found in the average church, like the First Baptist Church of Collegetown, along with the sad events and potential practices of godless and fleshly uprisings in business meetings.

The practice of discipline

Finally, we saw that the doctrines of Calvinism will strengthen the concern and power of the local church to practise reformative discipline.

With the concern to receive into the church only the elect of God, as far as man can ascertain who they are, there will be also a burden for the membership to manifest the truth of that election and regeneration in their everyday lives. Some will still get into the church who are not the elect of God, and they must be disciplined and dealt with. Others, who are true believers, will struggle with sin and need to learn discipline, which in many cases can only be learned as the church imposes it with firmness and love as members sin. The primary purpose of discipline is always the glory of God — to purify his church by the restoration of the fallen member, or as a last resort, to purify his church by severing relationship with the unrepentant fallen member.

On the basis of these convictions, we entered upon our new life together in marriage on the last Sunday of the year. We were confident that God had brought us together in his sovereignty! We were confident that we would labour together for his glory in the ministry of the Word. I found that these doctrines gave me even a greater joy and commitment as I spoke my vows: 'I, Ira Fife Pointer, take thee, Terry Lynn Lasitor...'

As we left the church after the reception, the question crossed my mind, 'What theological search shall I make next?' The answer came immediately — 'Eschatology?' Then I wondered why I always seemed to choose the controversial subjects to research!

Understandably I didn't mention my thoughts on the possibility of a second search to Terry at that time. There would be enough time for that — later!

Subject index

Scripture index